BUILD YOUR OWN
CARTS & WAGONS:
15 PLANS & PROJECTS

BY WILLIAM L. SULLIVAN

TAB BOOKS Inc.
BLUE RIDGE SUMMIT, PA. 17214

Contents

Introduction

A TWO-WHEELED CART CAN BE A SIMPLE ANSWER to many transportation problems, whether you hook it up to a bicycle, horse, dog, wheelchair, or push it yourself. It's also an affordable and enjoyable way to travel.

Although carts alone will not solve our energy problems or the transportation crisis facing our cities, it's astonishing how much they *can* do. Carts have been successfully transporting people and goods for thousands of years. Today their future may be brighter than ever, simply because they're such a pleasant way of doing more with less.

Here are complete plans for 15 carts, ranging from leisurely Saturday projects to top-of-the-line models. All plans call for easily available materials and use tools found in the average shop, so you don't have to be a pro to get started. Most carts can be built for as little as $20 if you can find a set of used bike wheels.

The first project, a flower cart or serving cart, takes less than five hours from start to finish. This four-wheeler is handy around the greenhouse, shop, or kitchen. It can be put together by a beginner with nothing more than a hammer and a saw.

The next two projects have small bicycle wheels that make them easy to pull on longer, rougher jobs—as a garden cart for chores around the yard, or as a bicycle trailer for trips around town. These two feature a bolted wooden frame that's easily built with basic woodworking skills.

There are plans for 12 steel-frame carts. These carts are tougher than their wood-frame counterparts, yet surprisingly simple to build. Even if you have no experience working with metal, you can tackle one of these projects. All the materials can be bought at the local hardware store. Even the pipe is simply electrical conduit, a pregalvanized lightweight metal tubing that's easy to work with. The only special tool you'll need is an electrician's pipe bender to make curves without kinking the tube. If you can't borrow one, they cost less than $20 new. You won't need any heavy machinery to make the metal plates that hold the cart's axles. They're nothing more than electrical conduit box covers; you'll find them at the hardware store right next to the pipe.

Once the metal frames are bent, you can put them together by bolting, brazing, or welding them. All you need is a drill and a wrench if you're planning to bolt the frame. Brazing is a little stronger. It involves heating the joints and melting brazing rod metal onto the pieces to be joined. Most metalworking shops will have the equipment this requires.

Welding makes the strongest cart of all. The metal of the joints is actually fused together, either with an electric arc or a gas torch. Here the joints are so strong that the pipe itself would break before the weld would crack. Most of the carts built for this book have frames I have welded. I bought my little 50-amp arc welder new for just $60 and taught myself to use it in a week. If you bend the frame and have it all set up, you can have a professional welder do the job for you. It's only an hour's work and not too expensive for most carts.

Although the plans are given in both metric and English measurements, the systems are not interchangeable (to make the English units come out even, the carts had to be slightly redesigned). Stick to one system or the other.

Acknowledgments

The following cart builders have been kind enough to contribute material for this book. Special thanks are in order for Angela Thayer, Michael Hilton, Sherrie Hunter, Jim Pruitt of Lakeview Stables, Lynn Miller of *The Small Farmers Journal,* and the Isla Vista Recreation & Parks Department.

Bike-A-Boose Mfg.
PO Box 1088
Sandpoint, ID 83864

Bike-Hod Ltd.
29 Leslie Park Rd.
Croyton, Surrey CR0 6TN
England

Blue Sky Cycle Carts
29976 Enid Rd. E.
Eugene, OR 97402

Burley Design Cooperative
78300 Hwy. 99 S.
Cottage Grove, OR 97424

byKART Inc.
PO Box 8373
Fountain Valley, CA 92708

Cannondale Corp.
35 Pulaski St.
Stamford, CT 06902

The Carriage Works
Kellogg Star Rt. 11G
Oakland, OR 97462

Equinox Industries
1142 Chestnut Ave.
Cottage Grove, OR 97422

Garden Way Research
Charlotte, VT 05445

JHB Kits
10405 Wallace
Kansas City, MO 64134

Gerald Marsh
8704 Calva St.
Leona Valley, CA 93550

John Matt
80 W. Main St.
Chester, CT 06412

Paddy Products
PO Box 21003
Eugene, OR 97402

Pearsons
126 High St.
Sutton, Surrey SM1 1LU
England

Pedley Equipment
Shirehill Works
Saffron Walden, Essex CB11 3AL
England

Pelican Trailers
15210 Stagg St.
Van Nuys, CA 91405

Diane Petersen
Bayberry Knolls Bernese
109 Hollywood Ave.
Somerset, NJ 08873

Prototype Engineering
PO Box 4202
Chico, CA 95927

Vermont-Ware
Richmond Rd.
Hinesburg, VT 05461

W. C. Enterprises
PO Box 1688
Louisville, KY 40201

Chapter 1

Patio Flower Cart

HERE'S A FOUR-WHEELER THAT COMES IN handy everywhere it goes (Fig. 1-1). Outdoors it's a flower cart or a support vehicle at the patio barbecue. In the house it's a serving cart or a portable craft and hobby bench (Fig. 1-2). It's attractive enough to use at a restaurant to bus dishes, yet strong enough to cart books around a library or even shuttle engine parts around a warehouse.

This cart is very easy to build. A beginner can put together the 43 pieces of lumber with a hammer and saw in less than five hours. Add four casters and you've got a handsome cart for under $20.

LADDER-SHAPED SUPPORTS

To build this little roll-around, you'll need about 110 linear feet of 1 × 3 lumber, cut as described in Table 1-1. Because there are only four different lengths, cut one of each very carefully. Use these as patterns to mark the rest.

The cart rolls fine without a handle, but if you'd like it to have one, get a piece of 1-inch doweling and drill holes for it 4 cm (1½ inches) from the end of the two 90-cm (36-inch) boards. Rounding off the end of these

long pieces with a keyhole saw looks nice. If you don't have a saw that cuts curves, just saw a little of the front corners off straight at 45-degree angles.

Now you'll need 1½-inch nails, a hammer, and some wood glue to start assembling things. First build two ladder-shaped supports (Fig. 1-3), one for either end of the cart. Use 77-cm (30½-inch) pieces for the sides of the ladders and 50-cm (20-inch) pieces for the "rungs" that will later support shelves (Fig. 1-4). Before you nail anything down, lay it out and check the measurements to make sure everything's right. The "rungs" on the inside of the ladders should be 4 cm (1½ inches) *lower* than the outside slats. All the cross braces should be exactly flush with the side of the long boards. Check with a square (or something with a good right angle) to make sure it isn't crooked. Nail it together. Use a small bead of yellow carpenter's wood glue wherever the wood touches. Clamp each joint with two nails.

When the six "rungs" of the ladder are in place, add a bottom 50-cm (20-inch) board as in Fig. 1-3. You'll mount casters on this board after the rest of the cart is finished.

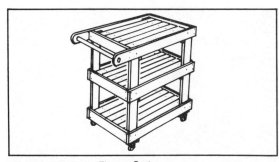

Fig. 1-1. The Patio Flower Cart.

HANDLE, SHELVES, AND WHEELS

Stand these two ladderlike supports on their sides, facing each other with their bottoms nearest you and the six cross braces that are 4 cm (1½ inches) lower facing in. Then position two 77-cm (30½-inch) boards between the two ladder supports as rails on the sides of the bottom two shelves (Fig. 1-5). These rails should line up with the *outside* ladder "rungs" and should fit flush on the ends. Check them with a square, then glue and nail them in place. After turning the cart over, nail rails on the other side to match.

Fig. 1-2. With plenty of room for plants, pots, and tools, this cart is perfect for the greenhouse or patio—or as a servicing cart indoors. It takes just five hours to build.

Table 1-1. Patio Flower Cart Materials.

Lumber
110' of 1 × 3 pine or fir, cut as follows:
    2-90 cm (36")
    8-77 cm (30½")
    18-73 cm (29")
    14-50 cm (20")

1" doweling, cut to 54 cm (21½")

Hardware
1 lb. of 1½" nails
wood glue
4 swivel casters
screws, if needed, to mount casters

Fig. 1-4. First step is to nail together two "ladders" of 1 × 3 lumber. These will be the frames for the cart's ends.

Think about the handle. If you don't want a dowel handle, just nail the 90-cm (36-inch) boards on the upper sides of the cart, much like the lower rails but with one end sticking out (this does make a type of handle) (Fig. 1-6). If you like the doweling and have a 1-inch drill, cut the dowel to 54 cm (21½ inches), daub some glue near its ends, and pound it into the holes you've drilled in the long rails. Position this whole assembly at the top of the cart and nail it on.

All the cart lacks are shelves and wheels. The shelves are made of 18 pieces of 1 × 3 lumber, cut to 73 cm (29 inches) (Fig. 1-7). Starting with the bottom shelf, lay out six of these slats. Space them evenly (about 1.2 cm or ½ inch apart) with the outside boards right up against the corner posts. Nail them in place—no glue is necessary here—and repeat the procedure for the middle and top shelves.

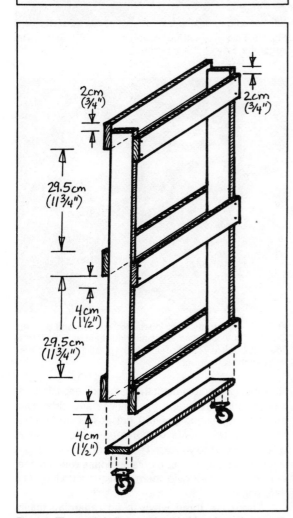

2cm (¾")
2cm (¾")
29.5cm (11¾")
4cm (1½")
29.5cm (11¾")
4cm (1½")

Fig. 1-3. The cart is built around two ladder-shaped supports. Shelf slats are nailed to the "rungs" on the right.

Fig. 1-5. Next add side rails to join the two "ladders." Then put on shelves made of spaced 1 × 3s.

3

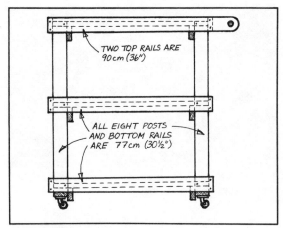

Fig. 1-6. Side view.

TWO TOP RAILS ARE 90cm (36")

ALL EIGHT POSTS AND BOTTOM RAILS ARE 77cm (30½")

Fig. 1-8. Finally, mount four swivel casters on the bottom. The larger the casters, the smoother the cart will roll.

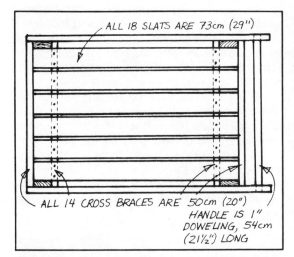

Fig. 1-7. Top view.

ALL 18 SLATS ARE 73cm (29")

ALL 14 CROSS BRACES ARE 50cm (20")

HANDLE IS 1" DOWELING, 54cm (21½") LONG

Fig. 1-9. Indoors the cart looks nice sanded and painted. Outdoors a wood stain is simple and durable. This cart is finished with a few coats of clear liquid plastic, making it easy to clean indoors or out.

Turn the cart upside down to put on some wheels. Ideally you've found a set of casters with ball bearing swivels at the hardware store (Fig. 1-8). The wheel diameter should be over 5 cm (2 inches) if you want the cart to roll smoothly. You can use either the type that attaches with screws or the kind with a post that fits up into holes drilled in the bottoms of the four corner posts.

FINISHING

You can leave the wood on this cart *au naturel,* but a little finish will help protect the cart and keep it looking nice longer. First, sand the shelves and sides with some heavy sandpaper (60 grit at first, then 110). Wrap quarter sheets of sandpaper around small blocks of wood so you won't get slivers in your hands. I like to touch up the sharp outside edges with a plane, but you can also give them a slight rounding with sandpaper.

There are three ways to go regarding finish. Choose an enamel oil paint if you want the cart to match your interior decor. A brown oil stain will never show dirt, even when the cart's used in the greenhouse or shop. A clear finish will show off the wood nicely (assuming it deserves it). Choose either varnish or a few tough coats of liquid plastic (Fig. 1-9).

Once you start putting this cart to work, you'll discover what a heavy-duty transporter it really is. Even the heaviest load of potted plants rolls right along without a sign of a wobble. It seems to serve equally well carting flowers or encyclopedias, laundry or scrap metal.

Chapter 2

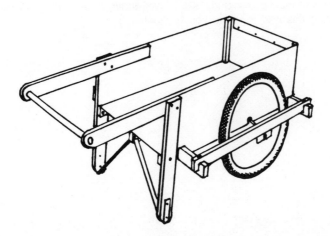

Wood-Frame Garden Cart

T HERE'S NOTHING QUITE AS HANDY FOR HAUL-
ling jobs around the yard or farm as a two-wheeled cart (Fig. 2-1). The cart can carry *three times* as
much as a wheelbarrow and is much more stable on
uneven ground. A well-designed garden cart takes the
weight of the load off your back and arms—one hand is
enough to push even a big load (Fig. 2-2).

   This cart is a project that you can put together on a
Saturday with a drill and saw for less than $20. Its
bolted frame is tough enough for most everyday
chores (for a heavier-duty cart, compare the Steel-
Frame Garden Cart in Chapter 11). It has a handle at a
convenient height, metal reinforcing on the struts and
front edge, and 20-inch bicycle wheels that are big
enough to roll smoothly over bumps or even down
stairs. The wheels are small enough to be strong,
particularly because their axles are supported on *both*
the inside and outside.

WOODEN FRAME

The cart's frame is made of notched and bolted 1 × 2
lumber (note that commercial 1 × 2s are really only ¾
inch × 1¾ inches or 2 cm × 4.5 cm). See Table 2-1.
Cut the pieces to length and mark for notches (Fig.

2-3). Make all the notches 1.2 cm (½ inch) deep and 2
cm (¾ inch) wide; saw down on the edges of each
notch and chip them out with a chisel. Pound the frame
together and check that the openings where the
wheels will go are just 11 cm (4½ inches) wide (Fig.
2-4). Drill ¼-inch holes straight down through the outside eight joints of the frame. Bolt these together with
¼-inch × 3-inch carriage bolts (Fig. 2-5).

   Next cut out the cart sides, bottom, and end from
¼-inch *exterior* plywood, as in Fig. 2-6. Carefully cut
slots for the wheel axles in the sides and in the outside
axle plates. Make them just wide enough for the axle
and 3.5 cm (1¼ inches) long.

   The bottom goes on the frame next. Notice that its
corners would cover up four of the frame's bolts. Take
these bolts out, position the bottom, turn the whole
frame over, and drill down through these bolt holes and
through the bottom. Glue the bottom in place. Secure it
by replacing these four bolts and nailing down the rest
of the plywood.

STRONG BOX

The end of the cart needs two pieces of corner molding
before it can be attached. Cut two of these 29.5-cm

6

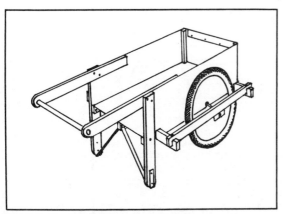

Fig. 2-1. The Wood-Frame Garden Cart.

(11½-inch) posts out of 1 × 1 lumber (2 cm × 2 cm) to serve as glue blocks between the end and the sides. Glue and screw the posts flush in the upper left- and right-hand corners of the end. Use ¾-inch wood screws; they'll go in easier if you predrill 3.5-mm or 9/64-inch holes for them in the plywood. Glue and nail the end in place. Then glue and screw the sides on, adding extra screws around the axle slots.

The outside axle plates go on the *inside* of the frame rail opposite the axle slots in the sides. The slots on these axle plates must line up exactly with the slots in the sides, or the wheels will be crooked. Turn the cart upside down and line up all four slots by dropping a straightedge into them. Mark for the axle plates. *Unbolt and remove* the outer frame rails before gluing

Fig. 2-2. This garden cart's design balances the weight of the load over the wheels—not on your back.

Table 2-1. Wood-Frame Garden Cart Materials.

Lumber
1 4′ × 8′ sheet ¼″ exterior plywood
21′ 1 × 2 lumber
9′ 1 × 4 lumber
1 1″ dowel, 57 cm (22½″)
2 1 × 1 molding pieces, 29.5 cm (11½″)

Bike Shop
2 20″ × 2.25 front wheels

Hardware
8 ¼″ × 3″ carriage bolts
6 ¼″ × 2″ carriage bolts
2 ⅛″ × 1″ metal bars, 54 cm (21″)
1 26-gauge galvanized sheet metal
   scrap, 12 × 52 cm (5″ × 20½″)
1 1½″ stove bolt
4 1″ stove bolts
8 ⅜″ metal washers
some ¾″ wood screws and short nails

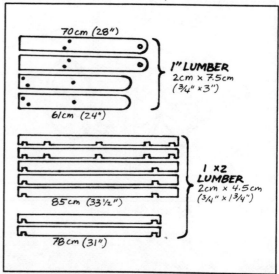

Fig. 2-3. Lumber cutting details.

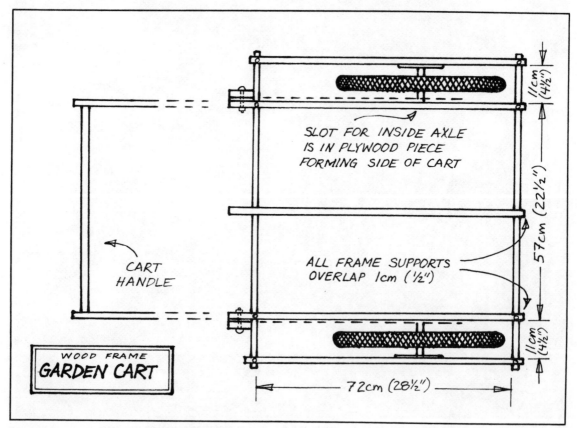

Fig. 2-4. Top view of frame (without plywood box).

Fig. 2-5. The cart's frame is first notched, then bolted together.

and securely screwing the plates onto them.

Put the struts on the front of the cart, using 2-inch carriage bolts to secure them to the frame. Then assemble the cart handle. The front of the handle is a 57-cm length (22½ inches) of 1-inch doweling. Glue the ends of the dowel and pound them into holes drilled in the handle sides. The handle attaches to the cart with four 2-inch carriage bolts through the struts and a number of screws through the cart sides. Position the handle about 36 cm (14 inches) in front of the cart.

When the wood parts of the cart are assembled, apply a good coat of oil stain to the wood to waterproof it and keep it from showing dirt. The wheels can go on when the stain dries. Because a pair of new wheels would cost at least $35, you may want to get a pair of

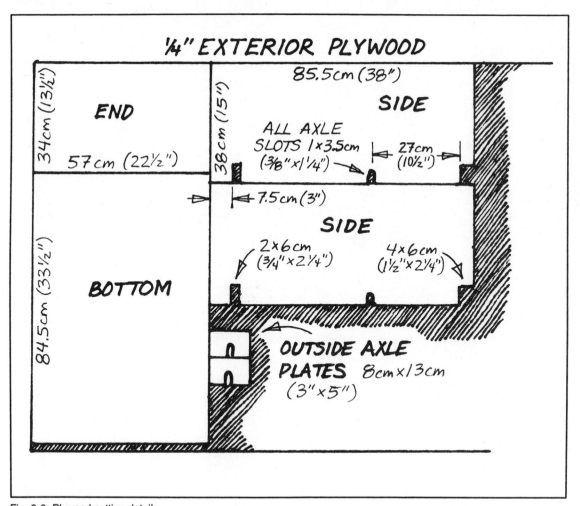

Fig. 2-6. Plywood cutting details.

used 20-inch front wheels salvaged from kids' bikes. Most repair shops dealing in used bikes will sell these wheels for about $2. Fit them out with fat 20-inch × 2.25 tires for working on soft ground. Put on the wheels. Use big metal washers to keep the axle nuts from chewing up the plywood around the axle slots.

METAL REINFORCEMENTS

A few finishing touches will add to the cart's durability. Bolt on some metal braces to strengthen the struts. Aluminum is easy to work with and is available at hardware stores in suitable 1/8-inch × 1-inch bars. Cut two 54-cm (21-inch) lengths and bend them over the edge of a table to fit as shown. Bolt them together onto the middle of the frame with a 1½-inch stove bolt. Wrap them under each strut to protect the struts' bottoms. Bolt them onto the outside of the struts with 1-inch bolts.

Make a sheet metal protector for the end lip of the cart (sheet metal shops will sell suitable scraps for a few cents). Cut the metal to 12 cm × 52 cm (5 inches × 20½ inches) with tin snips. Clamp it in a vise between a scrap of ¼-inch plywood and a board. Fold the metal over the plywood lengthwise so it will wrap around the edge of the cart nicely. Drill holes and attach it with pop rivets or short bolts.

Chapter 3

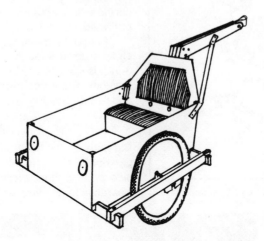

Wood-Frame Bike Cart

PERHAPS YOU'VE GOT SOME HAULING CHORES TO do. Maybe you need to pick up a chest of drawers or take a kayak in for repairs. You may have to take a child to the store. There's no need to borrow a station wagon or a small truck. All of these jobs can be handled nicely with an ordinary bicycle.

A bike is every bit as useful around town as a car is with the right cart in tow. The cart comes out *ahead* in many ways. It saves you plenty on gas and repair bills and *eliminates* parking problems, and it offers you the opportunity to get a little fresh air and exercise (although biking takes *10 times* less energy than walking). The community benefits, too, with less pollution, less traffic congestion, and eventually less need for parking lots.

A well-designed trailer is neither difficult to pull nor awkward to maneuver. It's possible to cruise level roads in high gear even with a full load. You'll probably forget it's there after a while.

There is a good selection of ready-made carts for sale these days, but why not trim their average $200 price tag by building one yourself? This Wood-Frame Bike Cart will only cost about $20 (if you can find some old bicycle wheels) and can be built in a weekend

(Figs. 3-1 and 3-2). It features plenty of cargo space, a padded child's seat with a safety belt, and even a toolbox hidden under the seat. The load limit of 45 kg (100 pounds) is enough for most household chores. If you need a cart for heavier jobs, take a look at the Freighter (Chapter 4) or the Bike Wagon (Chapter 5).

Like the other bike carts in this section, the Wood-Frame Bike Cart's strong hitch attaches to any bicycle in seconds—without tools—and fits tight without rattling. It's flexible enough that the cart won't turn over even if the bike takes a spill. See Table 3-1.

FRAME

To build this cart's frame, cut eight lengths of 1 × 2 lumber as shown in Fig. 3-3. Mark for notches that will be 1.2 cm (½ inch) deep and 2 cm (¾ inch) wide. Take special care with the two frame members that need six notches each. Space the center two slots exactly 2 cm (¾ inch) apart. Space the outside two notches on either side (where the gaps for the wheels will be) exactly 11 cm (4½ inches) apart. Check these markings with the drawing of the frame to make sure they're right. If you plan to use *rear* bicycle wheels instead of

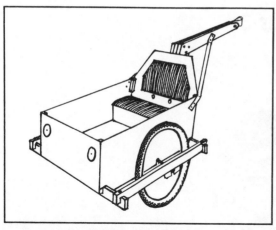

Fig. 3-1. The Wood-Frame Bike Cart.

front ones, the wheel gaps will have to be wider: 12.5 cm or 5 inches each. The remaining six frame pieces get notches spaced just 72 cm (28½ inches) apart. To cut the slots, first saw down along each edge, then chip out waste wood with a chisel (Fig. 3-4).

Pound the frame together and drill ¼-inch holes straight down through the outside eight joints (Fig. 3-5). Use 3-inch carriage bolts to hold these joints together. The inside four joints may be simply glued and nailed. See Fig. 3-6.

BOX

Cut parts for the box from a sheet of ¼-inch exterior plywood as shown in Fig. 3-7. When shaping the side pieces, check that the axle slots are positioned to allow clearance for the tires on both sides. If you are using

Fig. 3-2. Ideal for shopping trips, this cart makes a good weekend project.

Table 3-1. Wood-Frame Bike Cart Materials.

Lumber
1 4′ × 8′ sheet ¼″ exterior plywood
24′ 1 × 2 lumber
5′ 1 × 1 molding
3 small pieces ¾″ exterior plywood

Bike Shop
2 20″ × 1.75 front wheels
2 reflectors

Hardware
14 ¼″ × 3″ carriage bolts
1 ¼″ wing nut
2 ⅛″ × 1″ metal bars, 60 cm (24″)
4 ½″ stove bolts
4 1″ stove bolts
8 ⅜″ metal washers
some ¾″ wood screws and short nails
tire sidewall or neoprene (for hitch)

Fabric
1″ foam rubber scraps
vinyl upholstery fabric scraps
4′ of 1″ nylon webbing (for seat belt)
1 1″ slide buckle
2 leather scraps (for seat hinge)

wheels larger than the preferred 20-inch ones, you'll have to move the slots back a bit. Cut the slots just wide enough for the wheel axles and 3.5 cm (1¼ inches) long.

Put the bottom on the frame. It should be flush with the side and end support boards. Remove the four carriage bolts that the plywood would otherwise cover, glue the bottom in place, and secure it with several nails. Turn the frame upside down, drill *through* the bolt holes in the frame's bottom, and replace the bolts to clamp the bed to the frame.

Cut 1 × 1 molding to the dimensions specified in Fig. 3-7. Glue and nail the appropriate blocks to the edges of the plywood end, seat support, and back section (Fig. 3-8). Add a few ¾-inch wood screws (through predrilled holes) to clamp the joints tightly.

Glue and nail the end section to the rear of the frame. The sides can then be glued and screwed in place (add a few extra ¾-inch screws around the axle slots for strength). The back section can go in place, but make sure you've drilled a couple 2-cm (¾-inch) holes in it first so that you can install a simple web-and-buckle safety belt later. Install the seat support just far enough from the back, so the seat itself will rest

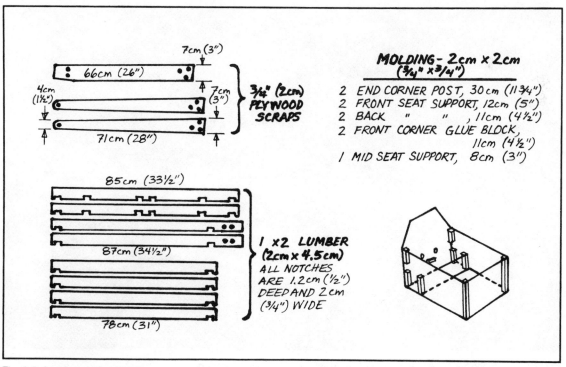

Fig. 3-3. Lumber cutting details.

Fig. 3-4. Notches in the frame are first cut with a saw, then chipped out with a chisel.

Fig. 3-5. The frame is pounded together with a mallet; joints are securely bolted.

on it and on the three little molding blocks at the cart's front.

The wheel axles will need to be supported on their *outer* ends and at the points where they enter the sides of the cart. You'll need the two outside axle plates shown in Fig. 3-7. They must be positioned precisely or the wheels will be crooked. To do this, turn the cart upside down and drop a straightedge into the side axle slots. The outside axle slots have to line up exactly with the straightedge. Mark the correct positions on the outer 1 × 2 frame members, unbolt and remove those pieces, glue and screw the axle holders down, and reinstall the assemblies.

TONGUE

The tongue support is a 7 cm × 66 cm (3 inches × 26 inches) piece of sturdy ¾-inch exterior plywood. If you have an unusually tall or short bicycle, you may want to adapt the length of this support to insure that the finished cart will be level when you connect it to your bike's seat post. Shape the support to fit snugly between the two central frame pieces and glue it in place. Clamp the glue with two ¼-inch × 3-inch carriage bolts through the frame and some wood screws through the plywood back.

While the support assembly dries, cut two pieces of plywood to form the tongue that runs from the cart to the bicycle. Shape them as shown in Fig. 3-9, with slight angles on the end that bolts to the tongue support, and with tapers on the tips that will be secured to the bike (to allow freedom of movement under the bicycle seat). Drill 8-mm (5/16-inch) holes in the tips where the bike connector will bolt on, 2 cm (¾ inch) from the ends of the tongue pieces.

FINISHING TOUCHES

With all the wood parts together, it's time to paint or stain your wagon. Staining is quickest and doesn't show the dirt, but a good yellow or orange paint job shows up better at night. In either case bolt on some plastic reflectors in back.

When the finish dries, you can pad the seat and make a back cushion. Cut scraps of 1-inch foam rubber to size, then trim pieces of vinyl upholstery fabric 5 cm (2 inches) larger on all sides than the foam. Fold the vinyl over the foam *and* the plywood. Secure it with ¼-inch staples or tacks. The easiest way to attach the finished seat to the cart is by stapling some scrap leather on the back as hinges, so the seat can be lifted like a lid.

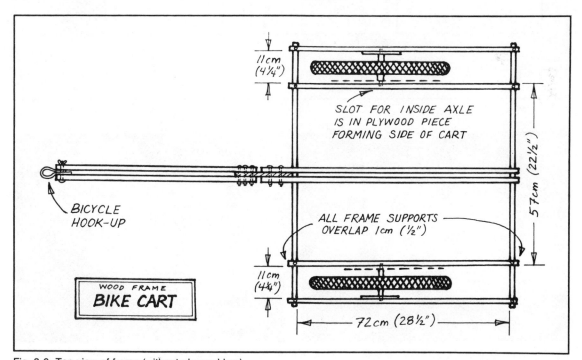

Fig. 3-6. Top view of frame (without plywood box).

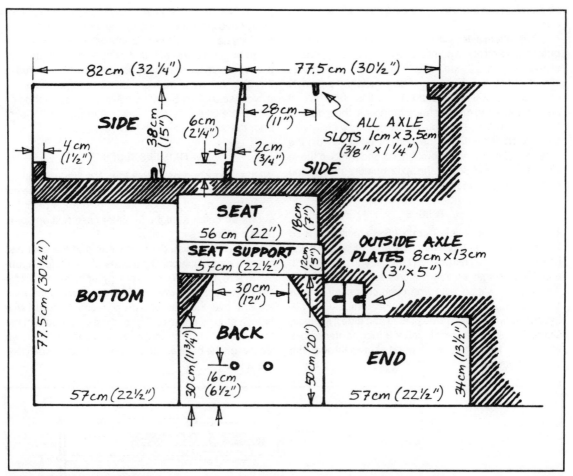

Fig. 3-7. Plywood cutting details.

Fig. 3-8. Glue blocks are glued and screwed in place before the plywood box is assembled.

Fig. 3-9. Before finishing, sand the cart and round the plywood edges.

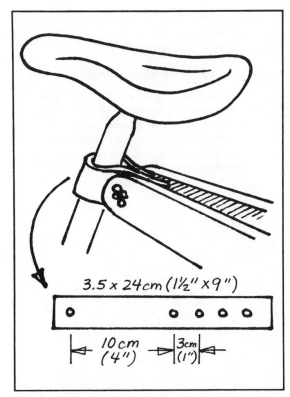

3.5 x 24 cm (1½" x 9")

|← 10 cm →|← 3cm →|
   (4")   (1")

Fig. 3-10. The cart attaches to the seat post of a bicycle with a strip of tire sidewall or neoprene rubber secured with a bolt and wing nut through punched holes. The holes should be 13 cm (5 inches) apart for most bikes.

Add a couple of metal braces to the cart's tongue to keep the trailer from wobbling under stress. Cut two 60-cm (24-inch) lengths of ⅛ inch × 1 inch aluminum or steel bar (available in hardware stores) and bend them. Secure the braces with ½-inch stove bolts

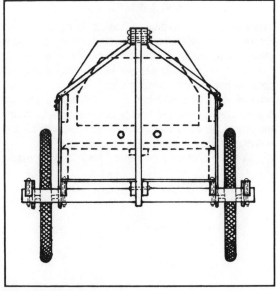

Fig. 3-12. End view.

through the cart sides and 1-inch stove bolts in the tongue.

For the lowest center of gravity and the greatest strength, choose a pair of front 20-inch bicycle wheels fitted out with light 20-inch × 1.75 tires. Put some big metal washers on the axles to keep the axle nuts from chewing into the cart's plywood axle slots. To cut costs, you can usually get 20-inch wheels from broken kids' bikes for a few dollars from repairmen who rebuild used bikes. If all you can find are 26-inch or 27-inch rollers, they'll work fine. Adjust the plans for them. Move the axle slots back to make room for the bigger wheels and shorten the tongue support, as the cart will be 3 inches higher off the road.

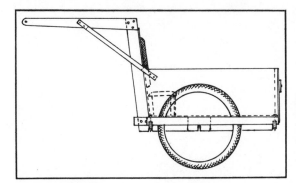

Fig. 3-11. Side view.

Fig. 3-13. The finished cart weighs about 16 kg (36 pounds) and can carry up to 45 kg (100 pounds).

BIKE CART HITCH

The simplest cart-to-bicycle hookup is nothing more than a strip of old auto tire sidewall, cut to length with a sharp knife, razor blade, or hacksaw (Fig. 3-10). Punch holes in it with a 9-mm (5/16-inch) leather or grommeting punch. Wrap the strip around the seat post of your bike and bolt its ends—trying various holes to get a solid, yet flexible connection—between the tips of the cart's tongue. A ¼-inch bolt with a wing nut allows easy unhitching without tools.

A more professional-looking hitch can be made the same way from three-ply neoprene belting. Industrial supply stores will sell suitable scraps for a few cents. See Figs. 3-11 and 3-12.

TRAVELING WITH THE CART

For the best ride, take it easy when going over bumps. Weight any heavy loads toward the front of the cart. Remember that your two-wheeler is now a wider, four-tired conveyance; take corners wide. It won't take long to get used to riding with a trailer in tow, even if you have demanding hauling chores to do (Fig. 3-13).

Chapter 4

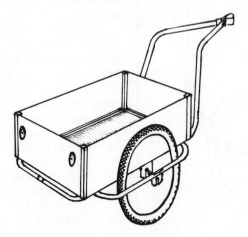

Freighter

THIS TOUGH, LIGHTWEIGHT BICYCLE TRAILER IS ideal for hauling groceries and laundry (Fig. 4-1). It is strong enough for the heavier stuff: bundles of newspapers, furniture, and loaded garbage cans (Fig. 4-2). It can take up to 100 kg (22 pounds) with regular 20-inch bicycle wheels. The load limit can be upped to an amazing 150 kg (333 pounds) with motocross-type 20-inch wheels.

The secret to such strength is a steel frame that is surprisingly easy to build, even in a home shop (See Table 4-1). Variations of this same metal bed can be used to build any number of strong, versatile carts for various uses.

BENDING THE STEEL FRAME

The cart's undercarriage is fashioned from three 10-foot lengths of EMT conduit (electrical metallic tubing). This lightweight pipe is available inexpensively at hardware stores and comes pregalvanized, so it will need no extra finish. The EMT is easily bent by hand with an electrician's pipe bender, a tool with a curved metal head that's screwed onto a pipe handle. Although this tool only costs about $20, you may prefer to borrow one for the few minutes you'll need it.

The first step is to bend two lengths of ¾-inch pipe to form the part of the frame that supports the box and also curves up to form the tongue. Mark both pipes as in Fig. 4-3 for the starts of the three bends. Cut the pipes with a hacksaw or pipe cutter at 228 cm (7½ feet). For the first bend, line up the arrow on the pipe bender (this arrow indicates the start of the bend) with the mark 13 cm (5⅛ inches) from the end of the conduit. With one foot on the bender, bring the handle down to make a 90-degree bend—as checked against a door frame or square (Fig. 4-4).

Turn the bender around for bend B, so you'll be bending the pipe *toward* bend A. Make this second bend at *almost* a right angle to the first. I've found the easiest way to do this is to put my foot on the first bend, with the tip of the pipe blocked slightly off the floor by a scrap of ¼-inch plywood, and then make the second bend perfectly vertical, raising the far end of the conduit up in the air until it's about 80 degrees from the floor.

For bend C, the final bend, hold the conduit in the position it will have when it's in the cart. Turn the pipe bender *upside down*, with the end of its handle on the floor and the arrow on the head matched with the third

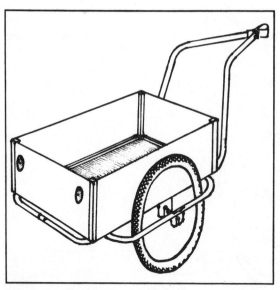

Fig. 4-1. The Freighter.

mark on the conduit, as in Fig. 4-5. Remember that the two sides of the cart's tongue have to come together at the hitch, so aim the bender slightly toward what will be the center. Bend the end of the pipe down until it's level with the floor when the rest of the frame is level.

Because the second half of this frame is a mirror image of the first, you'll make all the bends in the same places. Be sure the end of the conduit faces the opposite direction when you make bends B and C.

Don't worry if the bends aren't perfect; you can still bend them a little bit either way by hand. To check them, join the two pipes with an EMT coupling and separate the two sides of the frame with a spacer bar—a wood scrap exactly 53.3 cm (21 inches) long. The tips of the pipes that will be the cart's tongue should almost touch, centered 58 cm (23 inches) off the floor when the frame is resting on the ground.

To finish the tongue, take the two frame halves apart. Pound the front ends of the pipes flat so they fit together for the hitch (Fig. 4-6). This will create sharp

Fig. 4-2. Large loads tie down easily to the bumpers of this tough bicycle cart.

Lumber
1 4′ × 8′ sheet exterior ¼″ plywood
4′ 1 × 3 lumber (for molding) *or*
14′ 1 × 1 molding

Bike Shop
2 20″ × 1.75 front wheels
2 reflectors

Hardware
4 washers (for wheel axles)
some scraps of 26-gauge sheet metal
some ¾″ wood screws and short nails
tire sidewall or neoprene (for hitch)

Bolted Frame
3 10′ lengths of ¾″ EMT pipe
2 ¾″ EMT couplings
4 4″ × 4″ square electrical box
    covers (without "knockouts")
5 ¼″ × 2″ bolts
8 ¼″ × 1½″ bolts
1 ¼″ wing nut
4 1¼″ sheet metal screws with washers

Welded or Brazed Frame
2 10′ lengths of ¾″ EMT pipe
1 10′ length of ½″ EMT pipe
1 each, ¾″ and ½″ EMT couplings
4 4″ × 4″ square electrical box
    covers (without "knockouts")
1 ¼″ × 2″ bolt with wing nut
4 1″ sheet metal screws with washers

---

square corners that have to be removed, either by bending the tips of the corners aside with pliers or by grinding them round, so they won't cause wear on the rubber connector. Drill 8-mm (5/16-inch) holes for the hitch about 2 cm (¾-inch) from the tips of each half of the tongue. Fasten them together with a ¼-inch × 2-inch carriage bolt and wing nut (Fig. 4-7).

BENDING THE BUMPERS

The wheel housing is nothing more than a piece of ¾-inch conduit bent into a rectangle. If you plan to weld the frame instead of bolting it, you can use ½-inch EMT and save almost a kilo (2 pounds) from the cart's weight.

In either case mark for the four bends as in Fig. 4-3 and cut the pipe at 266.5 cm (8 feet 9 inches). Line up the arrow on the bender with your marks on the pipe, make each of the four bends in the same direction, and all to just 90 degrees. The final bend should bring the ends of the pipe to touch, where they can be

joined with an EMT coupling. Check the inside dimension of the rectangle against Fig. 4-3 and set the pipe aside while you make some axle plates to attach the wheels to the frame.

AXLE PLATES

You'll find the material for these plates with the other electrical supplies at the hardware store. They're 4-inch × 4-inch square conduit box covers. Get the ones without "knockouts" for holes in the center (Fig. 4-8). Avoid Steel City brand (they won't bend). Most plates have little slots in the corners for screws, but you can easily clip these off with tin snips or a hacksaw.

Cut slots in the plates for the axles. Make these slots 4 cm or 1½ inches long for bolted frames and 6.5 cm or 2½ inches long for welded or brazed frames. To cut them out, drill a 1-cm (⅜-inch) hole in each plate. Saw down to the hole on either side of the slot (Fig. 4-9).

For bolted frames only, clamp the edge of the plate in a vise against a piece of ¾-inch conduit. Bend the plate over the pipe with the palm of your hand until it curls snugly three-quarters of the way around the pipe (Fig. 4-10). Repeat for all four plates.

If you're planning on welding or brazing the plates on, bend them differently. For the inside axle plates, clamp 3 mm (⅛ inch) of the edge of the plate in a vise so the slot is pointing up. Bend the plate over to a 45-degree angle. For the outside units, clamp 15 mm (⅝ inch) of the edge in the vise and bend them all the way over to a 90-degree angle (Fig. 4-11).

GETTING THE FRAME TOGETHER

To clamp things down for welding or bolting, it's easiest to lay out the main part of the frame *upside down* on a table. Position the wheel housing on top (it will be on the *bottom* of the finished undercarriage). Center it front to back and check that the gaps for the wheels are the same on either side, but not less than 8.5 cm (3½ inches) nor more than 10 cm (4 inches wide).

Position the axle plates on the side of these wheel gaps. Center them exactly and check to make sure there will be clearance for the wheels. Align them all so the wheels won't be crooked. Dropping a straightedge into all four slots (as in Fig. 4-12) may help.

If you're bolting the frame, drill ¼-inch holes and use ¼-inch × 2-inch bolts to secure the wheel housing to the frame. Each of the axle plates gets two ¼-inch × 1½-inch bolts mounted *horizontally*. This way each

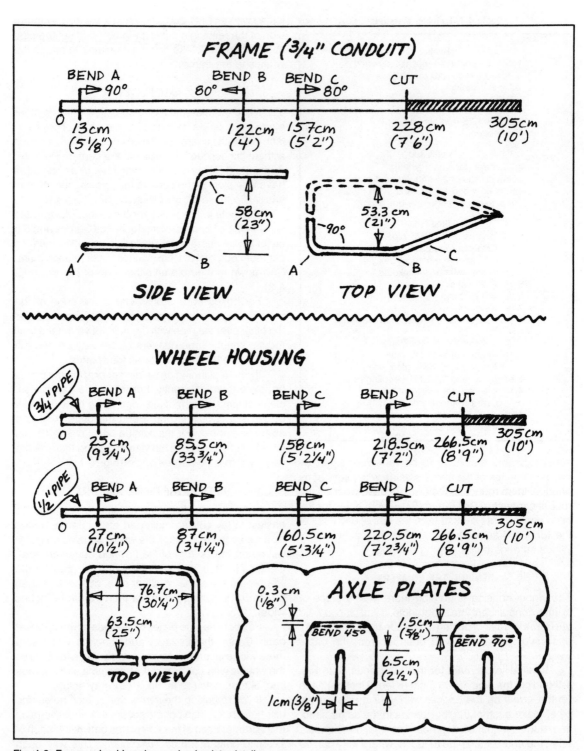

Fig. 4-3. Frame, wheel housing, and axle plate details.

Fig. 4-4. A pipe bending tool makes curves without kinks—here, the first bend of the frame.

Fig. 4-5. For the third bend of the frame, turn the pipe bender upside down and pull on the conduit.

Fig. 4-6. The end of the frame that will form the cart's tongue is pounded flat for the hitch.

bolt goes through the inside of an axle plate, the frame, *and* the curled-over outside part of the same plate.

If you're welding, use a low setting and keep moving to avoid burning holes in the thin conduit (I set my arc welder to 50 amps and use 3/32-inch 6011 welding rod). Welding galvanized metal gives off zinc oxide fumes that can cause nausea, so only work in a *well*-ventilated area. Wear a filter-type respirator. After welding, remove the slag with a wire brush and paint all the welds to prevent rusting.

BIKE CART BOX

A good bike cart box should be both strong and light. The Freighter is built from ¼-inch exterior plywood (cut as in Fig. 4-13) and secured on the edges with special trimmed-down molding. If you have access to a table

Fig. 4-7. The finished hitch is strong, yet flexible. It's made of a strip of tire sidewall or neoprene belting and is clamped with a bolt and wing nut.

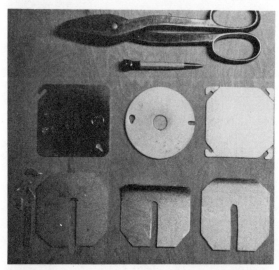

Fig. 4-8. Make plates for the wheel axles from conduit box covers like the one at upper right. Pass up round plates or those with "knockouts" (top center), and avoid Steel City brand (upper left). Finished plates, ready for welding, are at lower right and center.

saw, rip 1-inch lumber to make the molding as specified; if not, use 1 × 1 stock and shorten the side and end pieces 8 mm (¼ inch). See Table 4-2.

Glue the molding to the sides and ends. Assemble these parts and use ¾-inch screws to clamp and glue (in predrilled 3.5-mm or 9/64-inch holes through the plywood). Glue and screw the bottom in place. Add the little frame support blocks 5 cm (2 inches) from either end, where they'll brace the box against the frame. Sand and stain the box or paint it a nice bright color for visibility at night.

CORNER METAL PROTECTORS

An optional touch that will strengthen and protect the box involves folding some simple corner guards out of sheet metal (Fig. 4-14). You can buy suitable scraps by the pound at sheet metal shops. Cut them to the shape shown in Fig. 4-15 with a pair of tin snips. Fold the metal by clamping it lengthwise between two boards in a vise; you can easily bend it 90 degrees with the palm of your hand. Use pliers to bend the two tips of the metal guards so they fold over the top of the cart's

Fig. 4-9. Drill a 1-cm (⅜-inch) hole in each axle plate and saw a slot down to it.

corner post. Punch tiny holes with a nail or prick punch. Secure the units with ¾-inch wire nails. I like to add some hefty 1¼-inch galvanized nails—two into the molding at the very bottom, and one straight down through the top of each corner post.

Add some rear reflectors. Attach the box to the frame with 1-inch sheet metal screws (if the frame's welded) or 1¼-inch screws (if there are bolts in the way). You may have to angle the 3.5-mm (9/64-inch) pilot holes for the screws to really sink into the frame

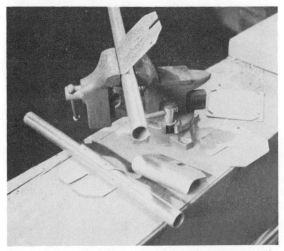

Fig. 4-10. For a bolted frame, bend the axle plates around a piece of pipe in a vise. Drill for bolt holes.

Fig. 4-11. Bend axle plates for a welded frame by clamping them directly in a vise.

25

Fig. 4-12. Position and clamp the frame when it's upside down. It's easiest to line up the axle plates by dropping a straight stick into the slots.

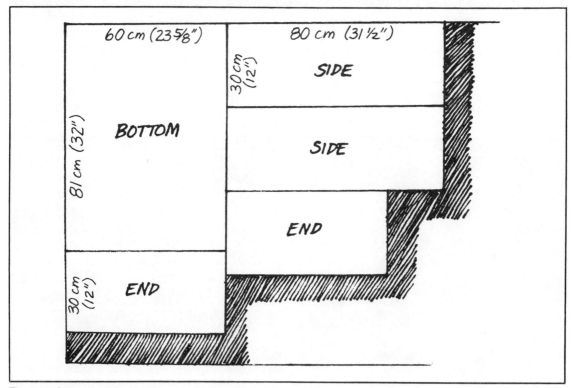

Fig. 4-13. Plywood cutting details.

Table 4-2. Molding Details.

Molding
1.5 cm × 1.5 cm (⅝″ × ⅝″)
4 corner posts, 30 cm (12″)
1.5 cm × 1.9 cm (⅝″ × ¾″)
2 side molding, 77 cm (30⅜″)
2 end molding, 55.7 cm (22″)
1.9 cm × 2.3 cm (¾″ × 1″)
2 frame support blocks, 6 cm (2″)

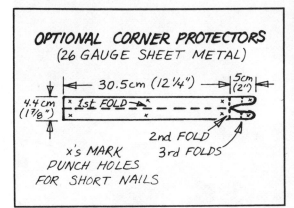

Fig. 4-14. Optional corner protectors.

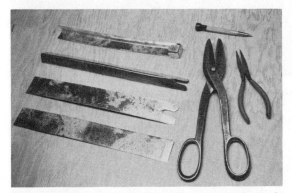

Fig. 4-15. Metal protectors for the cart's corners can be made with tin snips and pliers. The prick punch helps punch nail holes.

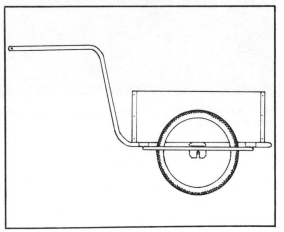

Fig. 4-16. The final step: putting on the wheels. Use washers to help the axle nuts cinch up tight.

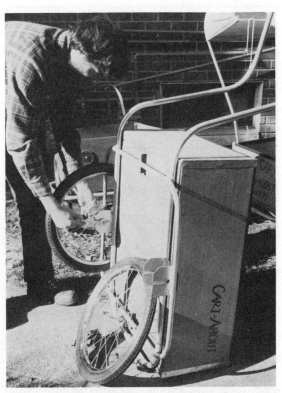

Fig. 4-17. Side view.

and still have room for metal washers under the screwheads.

Finish up by putting on a pair of 2-inch front wheels (Fig. 4-16). Add a hitch cut from tire sidewall or neoprene as described in Chapter 3.

To insure that your first ride with the Freighter goes smoothly, remember a few riding tips. Take corners wide to avoid clipping a curb. Go slowly over

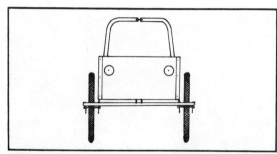

Fig. 4-18. End view.

bumps (and take them head-on). Make sure the bike's brakes are in good shape before you take a heavy load downhill.

The Freighter is an almost indestructible workhorse. Its clearance of 25 cm (10 inches) means you can haul it up curbs or over uneven ground. The bumpers on three sides make it easy to tie on bulky loads—even sheets of plywood. Because the Freighter only weighs 14 kg (31 pounds), it seems to follow a bicycle almost by itself (Figs. 4-17 through 4-19).

Fig. 4-19. The Freighter is both light and strong whether it has a bolted frame and stained box, as at left, or a welded frame and painted box, as at right.

Chapter 5

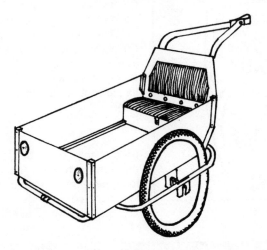

Bike Wagon

WHAT ABOUT THE KIDS? SUPPOSE YOU CAN'T leave them behind while you're out hauling groceries and laundry. Maybe you have to haul the kids around—to the day-care center, swimming lessons, or a toddler's birthday party.

The Bike Wagon may be the answer (Fig. 5-1). Like the Freighter, it will hold a couple hundred pounds of groceries, lumber, furniture, concrete block, or Christmas trees. The Bike Wagon also has a padded seat in front that will handle *two* children comfortably. The kids love it; the hardest part of every trip is convincing them the ride is over.

The Bike Wagon may also be the *safest* way to take kids by bicycle (although the Mini-Wagon is even better for very small tots). Two seat belts loop through holes behind the seat to hold children securely in the cart. Because of the cart's low center of gravity and wide wheelbase, it is very stable. The cart would be unlikely to tip unless you cut a corner and hit a curb going pretty fast (even then the Bike Wagon merely tips onto its side bumper). Even if the bike falls over, the hitch is flexible enough that the cart does *not* tip.

If you have more than two kids, you can also bolt a small car seat facing forward in the back of the Bike Wagon. An infant can be harnessed securely into the car seat while the older kids ride up front.

The seat is also comfortable for an adult, if he or she is unable or unwilling to ride a bike, or is perhaps just in for a pleasant ride. I use the Bike Wagon to take my wife and our small daughter down to the train station with all their baggage. I've also seen a Bike Wagon carrying *two* adults—one on the seat and one sitting cross-legged on the floor (this cart had indoor-outdoor *carpeting*). There was no problem, because the cart can handle 100 kg (222 pounds) with regular wheels and 150 kg (333 pounds) with motocross-type wheels.

Another handy feature of the Bike Wagon is the locking toolbox hidden under the seat (Fig. 5-2). Unless they're locked up, tool kits and bicycle pumps on bicycles have a tendency to disappear. The toolbox is also the perfect place for a camera or a sack lunch. The toolbox is big enough to lock up small purchases or important papers while shopping or at work.

There's no need to put this cart away when it rains. The covered wagon top (Chapter 6) attaches quickly and will keep kids and cargo dry in even the wettest weather. The buggy top (Chapter 7) is tall

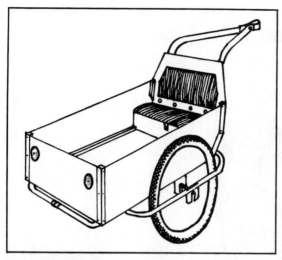

Fig. 5-1. The Bike Wagon.

enough for an adult, yet still provides reasonable protection from sun and rain. Both tops are streamlined so that their wind resistance is minimal except on really windy days. Both tops can be untied in seconds, folded up, and stowed in the toolbox.

The Bike Wagon is almost as easy to build as the Freighter; it's really just a Freighter with a seat in front. You need to cut a few plywood pieces that aren't simply rectangular, make different corner protectors for the front corners, and put in some upholstery (Table 5-1).

BOX

It's probably best to build the box first and then bend the frame to match it. The angle of the seat's back has to be the same as the angle of the frame, so they fit together nicely.

Start by laying out the plywood pieces as in Fig.

Fig. 5-2. A couple of kids, a heavy load, or even an adult can ride comfortably in this bicyclist's version of the family station wagon. The 16-kg (36-pound) cart features a lockable toolbox under the padded seat.

Table 5-1. Bike Wagon Materials.

Lumber
1 4' × 8' sheet ¼" exterior plywood
4' 1 × 3 lumber (for molding), *or*
11' of 1 × 1 molding

Bike Shop
2 20" × 1.75 front wheels
2 reflectors

Steel Frame
For frame materials, see Table 4-1

Hardware
4 washers (for wheel axles)
1 small hasp   2 small hinges
some ¼" staple gun staples (or tacks)
4 ½" stove bolts or pop rivets
some scraps of 26-gauge galvanized sheet metal
some ¾" wood screws and short nails
2 1" or 1¼" sheet metal screws with
washers (additional for frame)
tire sidewall or neoprene (for hitch)

Fabric
1" foam rubber scraps
vinyl upholstery fabric scraps
7' of 1" nylon webbing (for seat belts)
2 1" slide buckles

5-3. Then cut out the 12 pieces of molding for glue blocks (Fig. 5-4). They can all be easily ripped from 1-inch lumber on a table saw, or you can get by with heavier 1 × 1 molding by shortening the end bottom molding to 54.9 cm (21 ⅝ inches).

Glue and screw the molding to the plywood before assembling the box (Fig. 5-5). Anchor short pieces with one ¾-inch wood screw and longer pieces with more screws. Predrill holes in the plywood for the screws with a 3.5-mm (9/64-inch) bit. The glue can be further clamped with short nails or #10 carpet tacks.

First, put the end corner posts on the sides of the cart flush with the end. The side bottom molding butts up against the corner posts. Center the end bottom molding piece on the end, and you can glue the first three sides of the cart together.

Next comes the seat support. Glue and screw its moldings on and attach the unit between the two sides where the front of the toolbox will be.

Put on the bottom. Predrill holes for screws, spread glue on the molding, and position the bottom flush with the end of the cart. I also sink big 1¼-inch galvanized nails through the bottom into each corner post and seat support.

Drill 12-mm (½-inch) drainage holes in two corners of the bottom (the cart otherwise holds water). Drill down from the top so the plywood will splinter

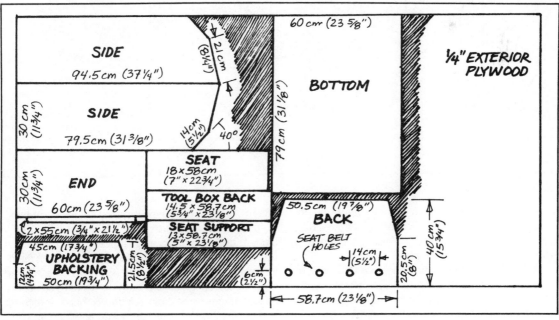

Fig. 5-3. Plywood cutting details.

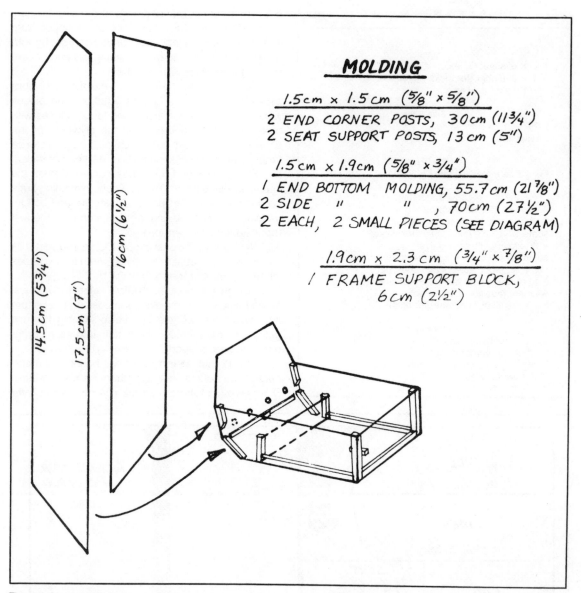

MOLDING

__1.5 cm x 1.5 cm (⅝" x ⅝")__
2 END CORNER POSTS, 30 cm (11¾")
2 SEAT SUPPORT POSTS, 13 cm (5")

__1.5 cm x 1.9 cm (⅝" x ¾")__
1 END BOTTOM MOLDING, 55.7 cm (21⅞")
2 SIDE   "   "   , 70 cm (27½")
2 EACH, 2 SMALL PIECES (SEE DIAGRAM)

__1.9 cm x 2.3 cm (¾" x ⅞")__
1 FRAME SUPPORT BLOCK,
        6 cm (2½")

14.5 cm (5¾")

17.5 cm (7")

16 cm (6½")

Fig. 5-4. Molding details.

underneath if it splinters anywhere. Screw on the frame support block in the center of the bottom, 20 cm (8 inches) from the end, where it will give the bottom extra strength by resting right on the frame.

Putting on the seat back should use up the remaining odd pieces of molding. Lay them out on the toolbox back and the seat back the way they are in Fig. 5-4, so you can visualize where everything goes.

There are a couple strips of ¼-inch plywood yet to attach. The first one gives the seat hinges something to screw into. It measures 2 cm × 55 cm (¾ inch × 21⅝ inches) and gets glued and stapled (or tacked) so its upper edge is lined up with the tops of the back molding blocks supporting the seat (Fig. 5-6). The second plywood scrap gives the seat some support in the middle. It measures 2 cm × 5 cm (¾ inch × 2 inches) and is glued and stapled or tacked on top of the first strip and right in the middle.

Fig. 5-5. The cart's plywood sides are securely screwed to molding that serves as glue blocks.

Fig. 5-6. Staple plywood strips to the seat back to support the seat and its hinges. Remember holes for seat belts.

Drill seat belt holes in the back. Use either a bit and brace or a power drill with a 2-cm (¾-inch) hole saw attachment. Drill each hole halfway through, turn it over, and finish from the other side to avoid splintering.

The toolbox back and the seat back can be glued and screwed onto the cart. Use just one or two screws in each piece of molding; more will make them split.

PAINTING AND PADDING

Sand the box to prepare it for painting. You can either round the rough plywood edges or cover them later with tape or ¼-inch vinyl cap molding (available with paneling supplies at lumber stores).

I like to stain the bottom brown before turning the cart over to paint the box. Two coats of an exterior oil-base gloss enamel paint are best, sanded lightly between coats. Remember the most visible color at night is yellow, followed by orange. Finally, to make the cart easier to wash, you can add a coat of glossy liquid plastic or fiberglass.

While the paint on the box is drying, you can start work on the upholstery. Using the seat and the up-holstery backing plywood pieces as patterns, cut out 1-inch foam rubber for the seat and back with a pair of scissors. The black vinyl upholstery cloth should be cut 4 cm (1½ inches) *larger* on all sides than the plywood to which it will be stapled. You can save almost 1 pound from the cart's finished weight by cutting out the inside of the plywood upholstery backing; you only need a plywood frame here. Place the fabric face down on a table with the foam and plywood over it. Pull the fabric tight and staple it with ¼-inch staples (or short tacks) in place.

When the paint on the box has dried, the up-holstery backing can be screwed in place with four ¾-inch screws set in predrilled holes in the back. The seat needs a couple of small hinges in back and a hasp centered in front (Fig. 5-7). Screws ½-inch or ⅝ inch long are fine in the seat, because the thick foam will pad their protruding points. The screws for the hasp plate on the seat support would be nasty sticking into the toolbox, so use ½-inch stove bolts or pop rivets here instead.

METAL CORNER PROTECTORS

Metal protectors will make the corners tougher and

Fig. 5-7. Once the seat upholstery has been stapled in place, fasten on a hasp and some hinges. A drill with a screwdriver bit speeds up the job.

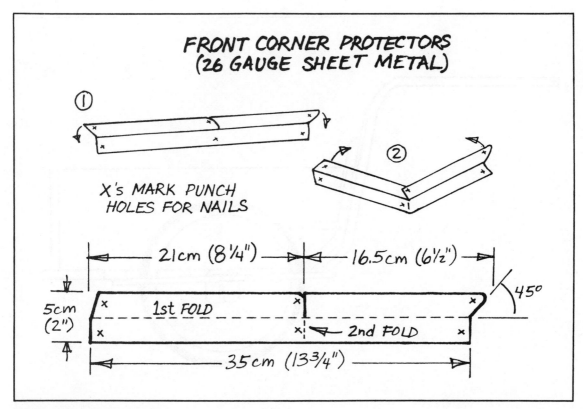

FRONT CORNER PROTECTORS
(26 GAUGE SHEET METAL)

①

②

X's MARK PUNCH
HOLES FOR NAILS

21cm (8¼") — 16.5cm (6½")

45°

5cm
(2")
1st FOLD

2nd FOLD

35cm (13¾")

Fig. 5-8. Front corner protectors.

hide the ragged plywood edges. You may be able to pick up a suitable scrap of light galvanized metal for free off the floor of a sheet metal shop. Using a scratch awl, mark the cuts and folds for two corner protectors as described for the Freighter in Chapter 4. Then mark for two protectors as in Fig. 5-8. Bend the Freighter-type protectors as described in that chapter. Bend the front corner protectors first lengthwise between long wood scraps clamped in a vise, and then by hand at the slit in the middle. Punch small holes for nails using a large nail or prick punch. Finally, nail the protectors in place with little ¾-inch wire nails everywhere except at the bottom of the back corners. Sink large 1¼-inch galvanized nails clear into the bottom moldings here.

The cart's box now only needs reflectors. I think two round ones in back show up well and look nice.

A FRAME LIKE A FREIGHTER

The Bike Wagon frame is identical to the frame used on the Freighter with one exception. In order to bring the center of gravity closer under the seat, the wheel

housing is welded or bolted onto the frame further forward. Instead of clamping the wheel housing so there's about 9 cm (3½ inches) between it and the rear bumper, increase this distance to 20 cm (8 inches). In this position the front of the wheel housing should come a little way up the front curve of the ¾-inch frame.

Instructions for bending the frame, cutting and bending the axle plates, welding, and making the hitch are in Chapter 4. While the Freighter box attached to the frame with just four sheet metal screws along the bottom, the Bike Wagon will need a couple more screws to go through the top of the seat back and into the frame there. Put on a pair of 20-inch bicycle wheels and roll the cart out of your shop (Figs. 5-9 through 5-11).

SEAT BELTS

Complete the Bike Wagon by adding seat belts for safety. Simply sew a slide buckle on a 3½-foot length (115 cm) of 1-inch nylon webbing. The four holes

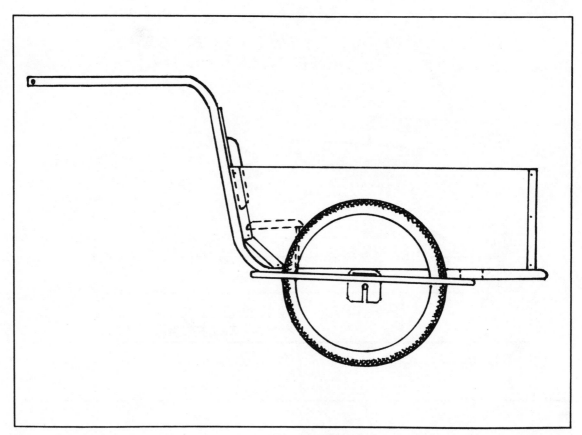

Fig. 5-9. Side view.

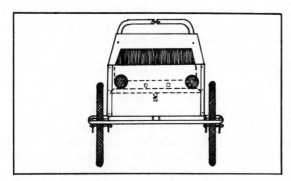

Fig. 5-10. End view.

Fig. 5-11. A load of plywood is no problem for the Bike Wagon.

behind the seat allow you to put in belts for kids sitting side by side or for a single child (who should then be in the center for stability.

Fenders can also be added to keep kids from touching the tires, although the danger here is not great (children wearing seat belts can't reach the wheel's spokes, which would be more hazardous). Fenders can be handy for stopping wheel splash from wet pavement. Instructions for easy-to-make fenders are in Chapter 7.

Chapter 6

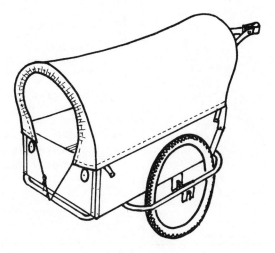

Covered Wagon

KIDS CAN ENJOY A BIKE TRIP EVEN IN THE RAIN IF they get to ride like pioneers in a covered wagon. Like the early prairie schooners, this design is light, keeps things really dry, and doesn't catch the wind (Figs. 6-1 and 6-2).

When the rain stops, the top is quickly untied, rolled up, and stuffed under the seat. The sides of the covered wagon top can be rolled up on a hot, sunny day to provide an umbrellalike sun shelter that doesn't act like a greenhouse. When the weather is nice, you can easily remove the two hoops supporting the top. They come off with a screwdriver and can be stored in a closet.

The Covered Wagon is tall enough for children up to age six (older kids and adults either can bike by themselves or will prefer the headroom of the Buggy). The top is *low* enough that it fits in the slipstream behind the bike rider with remarkably little wind resistance.

Once you have the materials together, the covered wagon top only takes a couple hours to assemble (Table 6-1). Hoops can be made of ⅛-inch × 1-inch aluminum bar (found in hardware stores) or steel, which is cheaper but heavier and can rust. The

10-ounce vinyl laminated nylon for the cover is produced under a variety of trade names and is sold at tent and awning stores, usually in 5-foot bolts. Consider nighttime visibility when choosing a color (I like bright yellow).

BUILDING THE HOOPS

The nylon top is stretched between two metal hoops that bolt onto the basic Bike Wagon. To make the hoops, first cut the flat metal bar into 5-foot lengths (152.5 cm) with a hacksaw. Drill two bolt holes at either end of each bar, 1 cm and 9 cm from the ends (½ inch and 3½ inches). Use a file to round off the ends slightly and clean off burrs from drilling.

If you try to bend the hoops freehand, they are likely to kink. The metal rim of a 20-inch bike wheel makes a convenient bending jig and curves the metal to the right shape (Fig. 6-3). Aluminum needs no finish, but steel hoops must be painted to prevent rust.

Mount the hoops with the top bolts close to the corners of the cart. If you bolt them on temporarily through just the top holes, you can adjust them until they lean out slightly and are just 120 cm (47½ inches) apart at the top (Fig. 6-4). When they're in the right

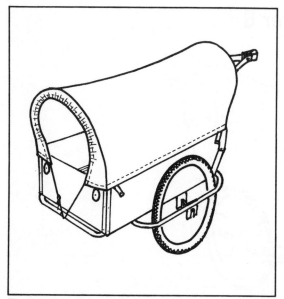

Fig. 6-1. The Covered Wagon.

Table 6-1. Covered Wagon Materials.

Fabric 5′ of 10-oz. vinyl laminated
nylon (min. 55½″ width)
thread to match

Hardware 10′ of 1″ × ⅛″ steel or
aluminum bar 8 ¾″ stove bolts with washers
and lock washers 15′ drawstring cord

position, drill through the lower holes all around and bolt these holes, too. Make sure to use a flat washer *and* a lock washer on the inside so the nuts won't chew up the plywood or rattle loose.

SEWING THE TOP

The top can be sewn on an ordinary sewing machine in about 20 minutes. First, cut the material according to Fig. 6-5 and get the two 230-cm (7½-foot) drawstrings ready. Then sew the long side hems, folding

Fig. 6-2. A covered wagon top is a fun and practical way to keep things dry.

Fig. 6-3. Steel or aluminum hoops can be bent to shape using a 20-inch wheel rim as a jig.

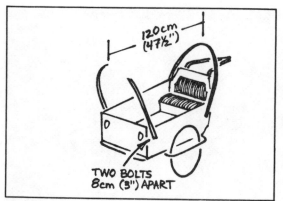

Fig. 6-4. Alignment of the covered wagon hoops.

Fig. 6-6. A covered top for the Freighter is also easy. It uses shorter hoop bars and a top that's cut square on both ends.

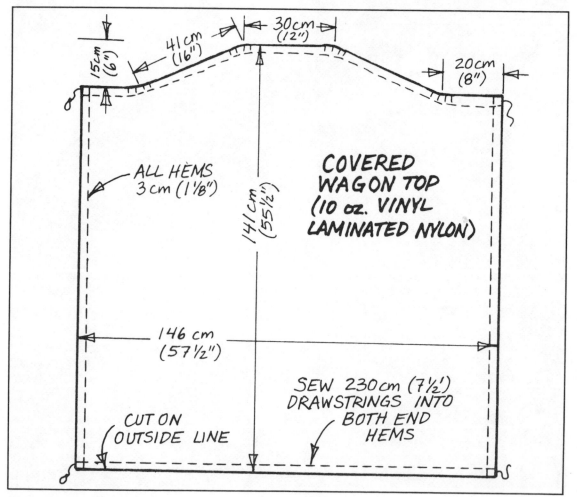

15 cm (6")

41 cm (16")

30 cm (12")

20 cm (8")

ALL HEMS 3 cm (1 1/8")

141 cm (55 1/2")

COVERED WAGON TOP (10 oz. VINYL LAMINATED NYLON)

146 cm (57 1/2")

SEW 230 cm (7 1/2') DRAWSTRINGS INTO BOTH END HEMS

CUT ON OUTSIDE LINE

Fig. 6-5. Fabric cutting details.

40

the material over 3 cm (1⅛ inches). Pin the end hems with the drawstrings in place. Cutting slits on the curves will make it easier to sew the front seam. Stitch back and forth at the ends to make the hem strong and to narrow the opening, so the drawstrings are less likely to get pulled inside.

Now you're ready to try the top on the cart (Fig. 6-6). The curved end goes in front, with the drawstring pulled tight and tied down around the frame at the bottom. Tie the drawstring on the other end to the rear bumper. With this done, the front opening should be large enough for a cyclist to keep an eye on the kids inside. The rear opening should be big enough for kids to crawl in without untying the top.

Chapter 7

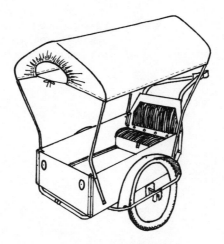

Buggy

THERE'S NOTHING WRONG WITH A LITTLE ELE-
gance, especially if it's as practical as this Buggy
(Fig. 7-1). Passengers ride in style through almost any
weather when a Bike Wagon (see Chapter 5) is fitted
with this simple top and a pair of easy-to-make fenders
(Fig. 7-2).

If the sun's too hot, the top gives shade and lets a
cool breeze through. When the rains come, put on the
rain pants and go biking. The cover will keep the riders
dry, and the fenders will stop wheel splash from the
wet streets. Even on a blustery day, the top's thin
profile keeps wind resistance down. The cloth top can
be taken down in just five seconds and stowed under
the seat.

There's headroom for tall adults. The passenger
can see out to enjoy the scenery, the bicyclist can keep
an eye on the load, and car drivers can spot the cart far
enough away to steer clear.

ADDING A BUGGY TOP

The top is supported by two hoops bent from ½-inch
EMT pipe (or ¾-inch aluminum tubing). Because each
hoop uses exactly 10 feet of pipe (and it is sold
10-foot lengths), there's no cutting involved (Table

7-1). Just mark for the five bends as in Fig. 7-3. Line up
the arrow on a ½-inch pipe bending tool with the first
mark and bend until the angle roughly matches the one
in Fig. 7-3. There is no need for great precision. If it's
within 10 degrees, the bend can be corrected later by
hand. Stand the pipe bender upside down for bend B,
with its handle on the ground, and bend the pipe down
over it. Bends C and D are simpler, but E requires the
upside-down treatment again.

Once the hoop's bent, check the measurements
against Fig. 7-3 and adjust things if necessary by
bending it over your knee. When it looks about right,
bend another one to match. Then mark for bolt holes
23 cm (9 inches) apart on each of the hoop ends.
Flatten the spot with a hammer first to make the drilling
go easier.

To mount the hoops on a Bike Wagon, first drill
holes in the cart's four corners, near the top of the side
and close to the corner molding. Use stove bolts with
washers and lock washers on these top holes to hold
the hoops in position. Angle the hoops out to the front
and back until they are just 140 cm (4 feet 7 inches)
apart at the top. You can drill through the bottom hoop
holes all around and bolt the frames securely to the
cart's sides.

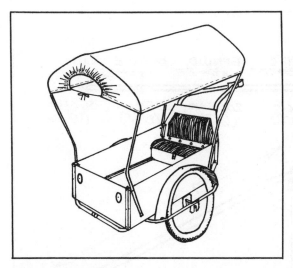

Fig. 7-1. The Buggy.

Table 7-1. Buggy Materials.

Lumber
some scraps of ⅛″ tempered Masonite hardboard
Hardware
8 1¼″ stove bolts with washers and lock washers
4 ½″ stove bolts or pop rivets
2 10′ lengths of ½″ EMT conduit
Fabric
2½ yards of waterproof nylon fabric (min. 55″ width)
8′ drawstring cord

Make the cover out of a waterproof, yet sewable nylon cloth. Cut and sew it as shown in Fig. 7-4. Try it out. The drawstrings cinch things up in front and back to take up slack. Mark for and sew little tucks or darts in each of the cover's four corners so the cloth follows the curve of the hoops at the bottom.

Fig. 7-2. Fixed for either rain or sun, a Bike Wagon with fenders and a buggy top is an elegant transport for this 6-month-old child, who is riding in a car seat that's bolted to the cart's floor.

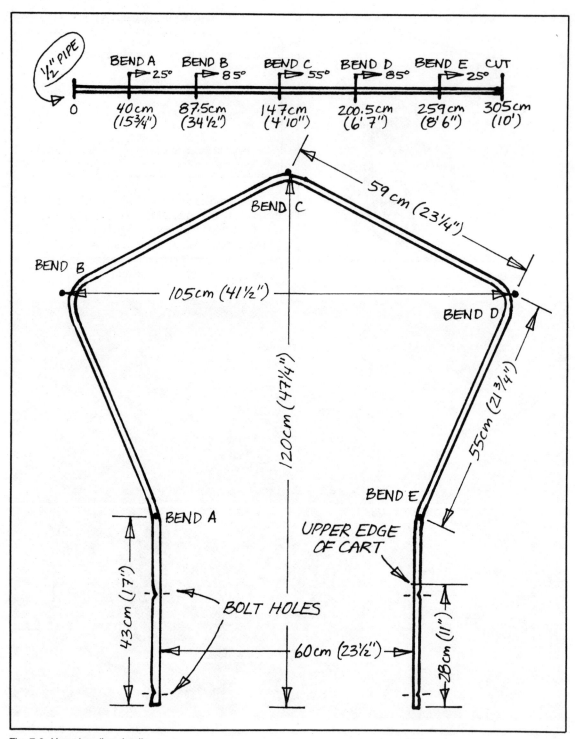

½" PIPE

BEND A 25° BEND B 85° BEND C 55° BEND D 85° BEND E 25° CUT

0 40cm (15¾") 87.5cm (34½") 147cm (4'10") 200.5cm (6'7") 259cm (8'6") 305cm (10')

BEND C

59cm (23¼")

BEND B

105cm (41½")

BEND D

120cm (47¼")

55cm (21¾")

BEND A

BEND E

UPPER EDGE OF CART

43cm (17")

BOLT HOLES

60cm (23½")

28cm (11")

Fig. 7-3. Hoop bending details.

44

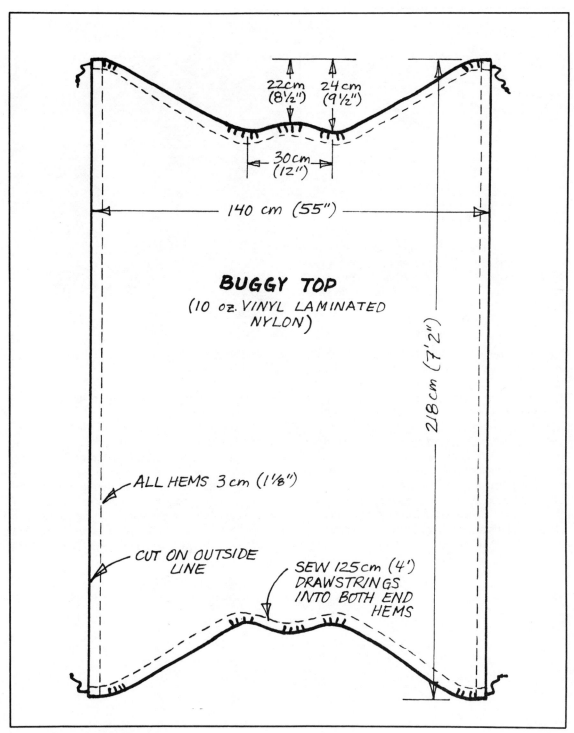

Fig. 7-4. Fabric cutting details.

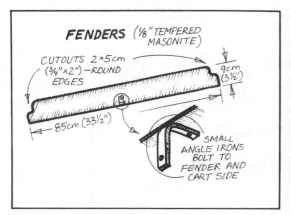

Fig. 7-5. Fender construction details.

You'll soon find that the drawstrings won't even need to be untied to take the cover down. The wheels splash mud up inside the cover without fenders, which is not so elegant, so it's time to make some wheel covers.

FENDERS

Mudguards serve the double purpose of keeping wheel splash away from riders and of keeping little riders from reaching down to touch the spinning tires. These fenders are made out of ⅛-inch thick tempered hardboard. This type of Masonite hardboard has been pressure treated to be both tough and completely weatherproof. It's also lightweight and inexpensive.

Cut the Masonite hardboard as shown in Fig. 7-5 and paint it to match your cart. Then make two little metal angle iron brackets to fasten the fenders to the cart sides (or you can buy brackets ready-made). I use the little scraps left over when I saw the slots out of the axle plates for the Bike Wagon's frame. Drill holes in either end of these pieces, bend them to a 90-degree angle in a vise, and secure them to the middle of the

Fig. 7-6. Adults find the Buggy has enough headroom and legroom for a comfortable ride.

long side of the fenders with little bolts or, ideally, rivets.

There's a trick to putting on the fenders. They must be bent to a U-shape in order to fit into the wheel housing of the cart, but they will crack if it's done quickly. Do it slowly. Take a minute or two to gradually arch the fenders to the correct position, giving the hardboard time to adjust. Once they're in place, bolt the little angle irons to the side of the cart. This gives them quite a bit of strength—which is good, because the kids are sure to insist on crawling around on them (Fig. 7-6).

Chapter 8

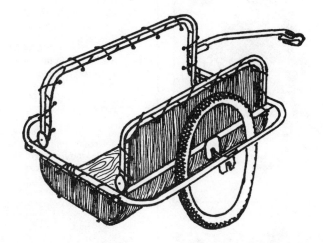

Bike Touring Cart

SOME PEOPLE SAY THERE'S NOTHING THAT CAN match the feeling of freedom and adventure which comes with touring by bicycle. Yet the bike tourer has to bring a lot of "home" along with him: repair tools, extra clothing, and usually a sleeping bag, tent, and cookstove. This gear often gets heaped onto the back of the bike, where the weight busts spokes in the rear wheel and turns bicycling into a balancing act.

More and more, bike tourers are taking carts like this one along to carry the load for them. This trailer is a good choice for touring, too, because of several special features (Fig. 8-1).

First, it only weighs 11 kg (24 pounds) (Fig. 8-2). The sides are made of nylon pack cloth laced to the frame.

Second, it has a very low profile, cutting wind resistance to almost nil and increasing stability. The bottom of the cart is slung *below* the axle to lower the center of gravity. This gives the trailer a clearance of just 13 cm (5 inches)—still enough to roll over small obstacles easily.

Third, it has a side hitch that connects to the bicycle frame just in front of the bike's rear axle. This allows you to load your bike with any style of pannier

bags or child carrier without having a trailer hitch in the way. Although it looks like the side hookup would limit how far the bike can turn to the right, even a stunt rider would have trouble riding a bike in a tight enough circle that the hitch arm got in the way. The lower hitch position helps with braking by throwing a little weight onto the rear wheel during stops.

Even those who never tour might still choose a lightweight, low-profile touring cart for trips around town, either because it's so easy to pull, or because they'd rather sew their cart than nail it together. This touring cart is strong enough for the heaviest loads. If you are handy with a sewing machine, you can add either a sling-type child seat or a tonneau rain cover.

TOURING FRAME

Electrical conduit can be easily bent and either welded or bolted to make a strong frame for this cart (Table 8-1). Aluminum is lighter, but it costs more and is a bit weaker. If you are a hard-core bicycle tourer, you may want to use it anyway, but note these differences. While ¾-inch EMT pipe suffices for the outer frame, aluminum pipe must be 1 inch in diameter, requiring a larger pipe bender. Aluminum can only be welded with

Fig. 8-1. The Bike Touring Cart.

Fig. 8-2. With his gear in a cart, this man is ready for a long trip. This cart is both light (11 kg or 24 pounds) and low to the ground to cut down on wind resistance when touring.

Table 8-1. Bike Touring Cart Materials.

Fabric
4' heavy nylon pack cloth
35 grommets, No. 0 size (¼" hole)
25' of ⅛" nylon cord

Bike Shop
2 20" × 1.75 front wheels
2 bolt-on reflectors

Lumber
a scrap of ¼" exterior plywood

Hardware
2 10' lengths of ¾" EMT pipe
2 10' lengths of ½" EMT pipe
1 ¾" EMT coupling
2 ½" EMT couplings (smooth-sided type)
4 4" × 4" square electrical box covers
    (without "knockouts")
1 ¼" × 1½" bolt with wing nut
1 ⅜" metal washer
tire sidewall or neoprene (for hitch)
4 washers (for wheel axles)
4 ¾" sheet metal screws
2 1¼" sheet metal screws

Additional for Bolted Frame
6 ¼" × 2" bolts
12 ¼" × 1½" bolts

the costly heli-arc process, so bolting may be required, even though this is not as strong.

The outer frame is made in two parts. The left-hand side will have the hitch; start with this piece by marking for bends as shown in Fig. 8-3. Do not cut the 10-foot length of ¾-inch pipe to length yet. Set the pipe bender with the arrow on the mark for bend A and make a 90-degree curve there. Then set up the second bend slightly out of line with bend A, so the hitch arm will rise about 8 cm (3 inches) from the level of the cart to the bike (study Figs. 8-4 and 8-5). Stop bend B when the pipe is at a 45-degree angle to the floor.

The third bend is another 45-degree angle, lined up again with the first bend so the hitch arm will level off before attaching to the bike. Cut off the scrap pipe with a hacksaw or pipe cutter. Pound this freshly cut end flat with a hammer and drill a 8-mm (5/16-inch) hole for the hitch bolt 2 cm (¾-inch) from the end. Remove the sharp square corners of the hitch end to keep them from cutting into the rubber connector when the bike turns; either bend the corners up with pliers or grind them round.

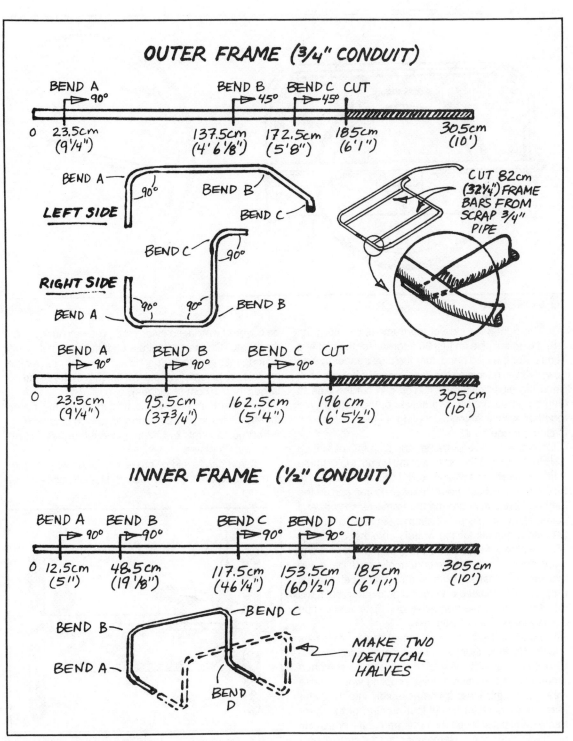

Fig. 8-3. Frame construction details.

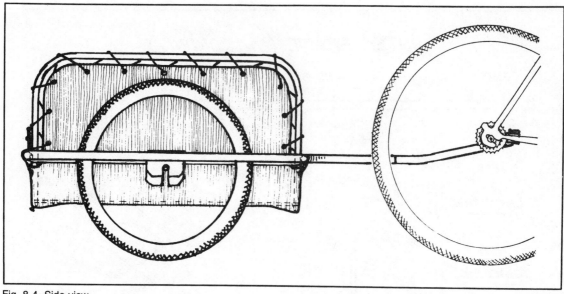

Fig. 8-4. Side view.

The right-hand side of the frame is simpler (Fig. 8-6). Bend the pipe up just 90 degrees for the first two bends. For the third bend, turn the pipe bender upside down with its handle on the floor, braced with your foot. Bend the pipe down over it. You can cut the pipe to length and secure the two halves of the outer frame together with a ¾-inch coupling in the rear and a C-clamp in the front.

To finish the outer frame, add a couple of ¾-inch bars that attach to the bottom of the frame. Make these from the scrap ends of pipe you just cut off. Cut them to 82 cm (32¼ inches), pound their ends flat, curl up the flattened ends to fit around the frame as shown, and clamp them in place. Position them with a 9.5-cm (3¾-inch) gap left for the wheels on either side.

The inner frame forms the sides of the cart and loops down to support the bottom plywood. Bend it in two identical halves from ½-inch electrical conduit (Fig. 8-7). You'll need a ½-inch pipe bender, but it will be worth the trouble borrowing one. The lighter pipe saves almost 2 kg (4 pounds).

Bend and cut the two inner frame halves as shown. Connect them with two smooth-sided ½-inch EMT couplings (the nylon cloth will later be stretched around this frame, and a bulky coupling would cause wear). Drop this inner frame assembly into the outer frame and check for fit. All four corners of the inner frame should just touch the outer frame. If it doesn't fit precisely, don't panic. Remember that the cart will only

be covered with laced nylon cloth; you can hush or pull the frame dimensions quite a bit before the nylon will no longer stretch to fit. Just be sure the gaps left for the wheels are no smaller than 8.5 cm (3⅜ inches) and no larger than 10 cm (4 inches).

By the time you clamp this much of the frame together, you're probably running low on clamps (Fig. 8-8). You can weld or bolt things together before putting on axle plates.

If you can't weld or braze and don't want to hire someone to do it, use ¼-inch × 1½-inch bolts to se-

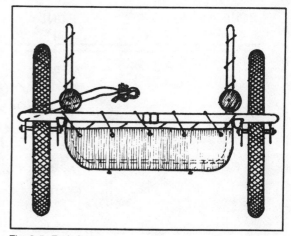

Fig. 8-5. End view.

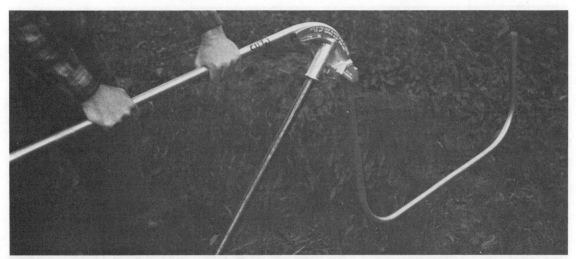

Fig. 8-6. The right-hand side of the cart's frame has three 90-degree bends—for the last one, stand the pipe bender on its handle as shown.

Fig. 8-7. The inner frame uses ½-inch pipe. Bend two identical halves and connect them with smooth EMT couplings.

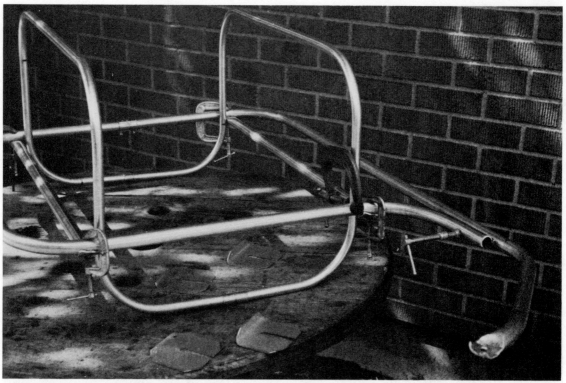

Fig. 8-8. Now the frame's ready for welding. If you run out of C-clamps, weld the frame together one piece at a time.

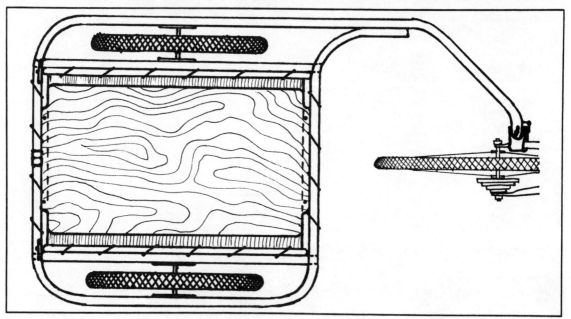

Fig. 8-9. Top view.

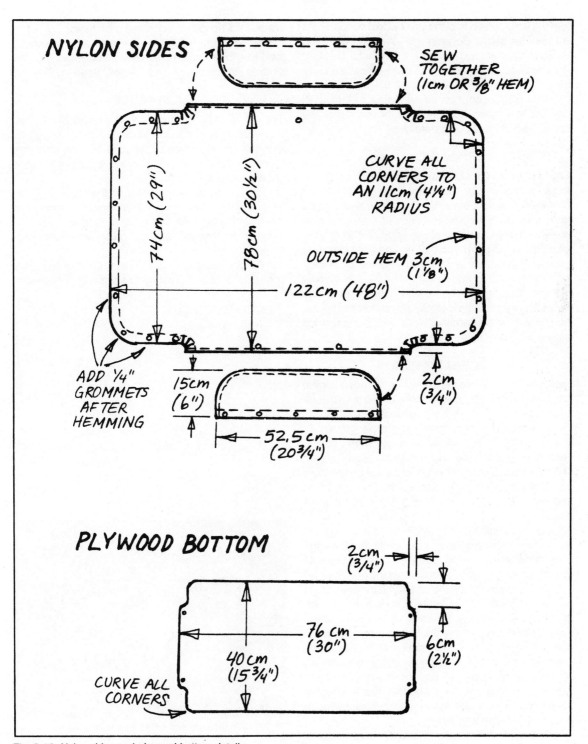

Fig. 8-10. Nylon sides and plywood bottom details.

cure the flattened ends of the inner wheel support bars to the outer frame. Connect the left- and right-hand halves in front with two ¼-inch × 2-inch bolts. Use four of these fasteners to clamp the inner frame to the outer chassis. Note the topview in Fig. 8-9.

Axle plates can then be added as described in Chapter 4. Position them right in the middle of the frame. Line the slots up carefully.

FIRM FLOOR

A solid plywood floor only weighs a pound, but some people prefer to save that weight and get along with the nylon pack cloth stretched taut underneath. If you have a featherweight bicycle without a kickstand or fenders and you are weighing your cart in grams, forget the plywood. If you plan to use your cart very much, however, cut a rectangular piece of ¼-inch exterior plywood as shown in Fig. 8-10—with cutouts in the corners for the frame and rounded edges to protect the nylon cloth sides. Sand and stain the board, then mount it to the frame with four ¾-inch sheet metal screws set in predrilled holes.

SEWING THE SIDES

Lacing cloth sides onto the frame has two advantages. The cloth is very light, and it can be pulled tight to look sharp even if it doesn't fit with precision.

Cut the sides from heavy nylon pack cloth as shown in Fig. 8-10. Sear all the edges with a candle flame to keep them from fraying. Pin the curved edges of the little end pieces to the straight edge of the larger piece. Sew these together with a 1-cm (⅜-inch) seam and use a second row of stitching to flat fell the ends down.

Hem the entire perimeter using up a 3-cm (1⅛-inch) seam allowance (this is enough to fold the edge over *twice* before sewing it down). Cut and sear slits on the four inside corners to make sewing easier there.

Try the nylon out on the cart frame to check the fit and mark for grommet holes. You'll need ¼-inch grommets about every 10 cm (4 inches) around the edge for the lacing. Also, mark for two more grommets right over the bottom of the frame back. Screws will go into the frame here to keep the nylon from wearing out when the cart is tipped on end for repairs or storage. Add one final grommet on the bottom near the front of the trailer. This one will act as a drain hole, because the cart otherwise holds water.

Clip tiny holes at each mark with sharp scissors. Use a grommeting tool (available at fabric or hardware stores for $1 or $2) to set all the grommets (Fig. 8-11). Finally, lace the fabric in place with an 8-meter (25 foot) length of ⅛-inch nylon cord. Pull it tight until the cloth is stretched taut on all sides. See Fig. 8-12.

FINISHING UP

The rest is easy. First, put on the wheels. Notice that the wheel openings in the frame are large enough for *any size* bicycle wheels, although 20-inch ones are recommended to keep the cart level and maintain a good clearance.

Bolt a couple of reflectors to the frame in back. Don't forget to put sheet metal screws in those two grommet holes at the bottom of the frame. I use 1¼-inch screws that stick out and protect the nylon from scrapes.

Finally, cut a 4-cm × 15-cm (1½ × 6-inch) rubber connector for the hitch out of tire sidewall or neoprene

Fig. 8-11. To set a grommet, first clip a small hole, then insert the two grommet halves and pound them together with a grommeting tool (above) and a hammer.

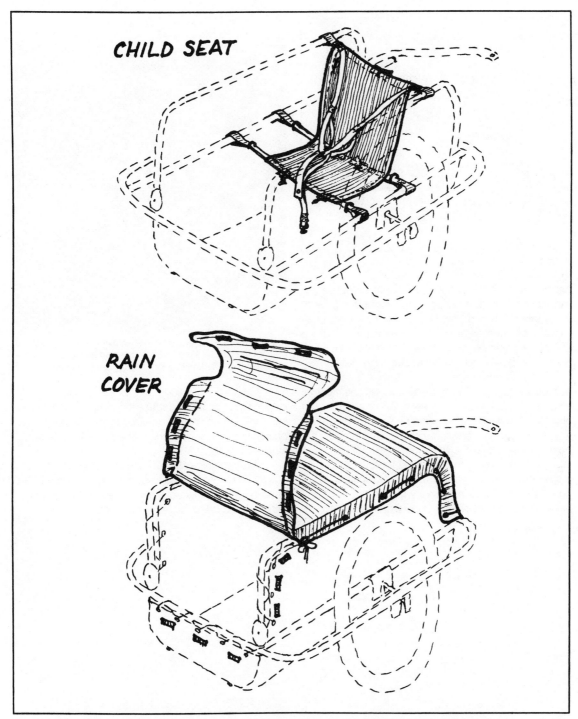

CHILD SEAT

RAIN COVER

Fig. 8-12. Two useful options can be easily sewn: a sling-type child seat that buckles to the frame through grommets in the sides, and a tonneau rain cover that laces tight in front and closes in back with Velcro fasteners.

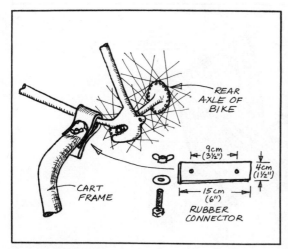

Fig. 8-13. Hitch detail.

Fig. 8-14. Straps or elastic cords across the open front and back of the cart keep contents inside and help in tying down large loads—without the wind resistance of a solid front and back.

belting. Punch holes 9 cm (3½ inches) apart using a 8-mm (5/16-inch) leather or grommeting punch. Wrap this piece of rubber around the bike frame just forward of the rear axle and clamp it tightly with a ¼-inch × 1½-inch bolt between the metal tongue of the cart and a ⅜-inch metal washer (Fig. 8-13).

If the hitch is properly snug, it will not be able to slip either forward or backward. It will be flexible enough to allow for turning the bike—or even for the bike to tip over without upsetting the cart. The part of the frame the hitch connects to is usually tapered. This helps to insure that the hitch can't slide forward.

When you take the completed touring cart out for a spin and, say, bring home a load of groceries, you'll notice that the sides aren't very high in the front and back. This cuts down on wind resistance and allows long loads to be carried with a low center of gravity. To keep the grocery bags from tipping out, strap a couple of elastic shock cords across the front and back openings (Fig. 8-14).

This cart holds almost as much as a Freighter, but it is 25 percent lighter and nearly *twice* as low to the ground. The cart is so easy to pull that it really deserves to be used for more than just touring.

Chapter 9

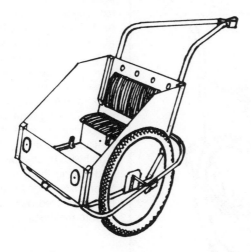

Mini-Wagon

GENERALLY, THE *SMALLEST* BIKE CART THAT WILL do the job is best. Shorter, lighter, lower, and narrower are words that describe the Mini-Wagon (Fig. 9-1).

One or two tots between the ages of six months and six years will fit snugly down in this cart's low seat, protected on both sides by tall plywood walls, and strapped in place with cross-chest seat belts (the kind used in car seats) (Fig. 9-2). Optional hoops for a covered wagon top can add extra protection for small children by acting as roll bars.

The Mini-Wagon is one of the most stable bike carts. It follows very closely behind a bicycle (it only extends 78 cm or 31 inches past the bike's rear wheel). The center of gravity is low because the cart's box is mounted *below* axle level; the inside axle actually goes through the side of the box.

There's less room for cargo. Two kids just about fill the cart, while toting just one tot leaves space for a couple bags of groceries. It's not the easiest cart to build; the smaller dimensions require greater accuracy to make things come out just right (Table 9-1). Nonetheless, if you are a confident builder and/or a

discriminating young parent, this little kiddy taxi may be just the right project for you.

BOX

Build a solid box of ¼-inch exterior plywood and molding cut as shown in Figs. 9-3 and 9-4. If you don't have access to a table saw to cut your own molding, you can use the heavier 1 × 1 lumber, but you'll have to shorten the end bottom molding piece of 50 cm (19¾ inches).

Clamp the glue on each piece with ¾-inch wood screws and short nails (Fig. 9-5). Make sure the curved axle openings in the sides and the bottom line up so the box can later be lowered onto the frame past the wheel axles. Don't forget some 2-cm (¾-inch) holes in the seat back for seat belts.

Sand and paint all the wood parts except the upholstery backing and the seat. You can be padding these two pieces while the paint's drying. Use 1-inch foam rubber cut just to size and vinyl upholstery fabric cut 4 cm (1½ inches larger) on all sides. Stretch the vinyl over the foam and tack it to the back of the

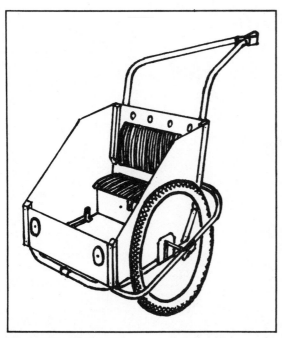

Fig. 9-1. The Mini-Wagon.

plywood with ¼-inch staples or short tacks. Install the seat with two small hinges in back and a little hasp in front, so you can open it like a lid or lock it up to store tools, seat belts, or a covered wagon top under the seat. Fasten the upholstery backing as a cushion above the seat. Use four ¾-inch screws through pre-drilled holes in the cart's front.

Finish the box by adding reflectors in back and sheet metal strips to strengthen and protect the corners. Make these strips from a 5-cm (2-inch) wide scrap of 26-gauge galvanized metal; sheet metal shops usually sell such scraps by the pound. Cut them as illustrated in Fig. 9-6 with tin snips. Bend them lengthwise by clamping them between boards in a vise and folding them over with the palm of your hand. Short nails will do for attaching these corners, but I add big galvanized nails at the bottom that sink into the bottom moldings.

FRAME

To cut down on weight, this frame uses two sizes of electrical conduit. Either borrow a pipe bender that adjusts to both ½-inch and ¾-inch EMT or get hold of

Fig. 9-2. The Mini-Wagon, shorter and lower than the Bike Wagon (at right), is designed especially for small children.

Table 9-1. Mini-Wagon Materials.

Lumber

1 4' × 4' piece of ¼″ exterior plywood
4' 1 × 3 lumber (for molding), or
  11' of 1 × 1 molding

Bike Shop

2 20″ × 1.75 front wheels
2 reflectors

Fabric

1″ foam rubber scraps
vinyl upholstery fabric scraps
10' of 1″ nylon webbing (for seat belts)
2 1″ slide buckles
2 size 24 snaps
2 small grommets

Hardware

2 10' lengths of ¾″ EMT pipe
1 10' length of ½″ EMT pipe
1 each, ¾″ and ½″ EMT couplings
4 4″ × 4″ square electrical box covers
  (without "knockouts")
4 washers (for wheel axles)
1 small hasp
2 small hinges
some ¼″ staple gun staples (or tacks)
4 ½″ stove bolts or pop rivets
some scraps of 26-gauge sheet metal
some ¾″ wood screws and short nails
tire sidewall or neoprene (for hitch)
4 1″ sheet metal screws with washers
1 ¼″ × 2″ bolt with wing nut

Additional for Bolted Frame

4 ¼″ × 2″ bolts
8 ¼″ × 1½″ bolts
4 1¼″ sheet metal screws with washers

two separate tools (they are inexpensive and available at electrical supply stores).

Mark two lengths of ¾-inch pipe for the outer frame and cut them to length (Fig. 9-7). For the first curve, set the arrow on the bending tool on the mark for bend A and make a 90-degree corner. For the second bend, turn the tool around and bend back toward bend A while making sure the pipe bender is at right angles to the first bend. Stop before 90 degrees on this bend to match the angle of the front of the cart's box.

For the final bend on this pipe, turn the bending tool upside down, with its handle on the floor, and bend the pipe down over it until the pipe is level with the bottom section of the frame. Remember to angle this bend in so the two tongues of the cart will come together in front.

Bend the second half of the frame at the same places, but as a *mirror image* of the first pipe. Then pound the hitch ends of both halves flat with a hammer, drill an 8-mm (5/16-inch) hole for the hitch bolt, and round off the sharp square edges of the flattened pipes by bending the corners aside or grinding them round.

Fit the two frame halves together with a ¾-inch EMT coupling. It's important that the two halves be just 50.3 cm (19⅞ inches) apart in the middle so the box will exactly fit on them. To make sure this dimension is right, cut a piece of scrap molding or lumber to this length. Put it between the two frame sides as a temporary spacer bar while the frame is being assembled.

The wheel housing is simply a rectangle of ½-inch EMT pipe, marked and bent as shown (Fig. 9-7). The inside dimensions of this rectangle must be right; check them and join the two ends with a ½-inch EMT coupling.

The plates that hold the wheel axles are made from 4-inch × 4-inch square electrical box covers (Fig. 9-8). First, use tin snips to clip off any dog-ears on the corners of the plates. Drill 1-cm (⅜-inch) holes at the ends of the axle slots. Saw the slots to the sizes in Fig. 9-7. Note that the outside plate must also be shortened by trimming it to 5.8 cm (2¼ inches). The inside plate has a tricky interior slot that can only be cut by taking the hacksaw apart and reassembling it with its blade through a hole in the plate. Finally, clamp 1.5 cm (⅝ inch) of the edge of each plate in a vise and bend them to a 90-degree angle so they'll curve around the frame nicely.

A bolted frame will lack some of the strength and rigidity of a welded chassis, but it can be built with just a drill and a wrench. Make the outer axle plate differently so it can be bolted on both sides of the wheel housing pipe. Cut the outer axle plate to 7.8 cm (3 inches) and give it a U-shaped bend on top by clamping it against a pipe in a vise and folding it over the pipe several times. Try putting this plate in place; its axle slot should not extend more than about 2.5 cm (1 inch) below the frame bar.

To position the whole frame for welding (or bolting), put the ½-inch wheel housing *under* the ¾-inch inner frame so that there is only 2 cm (¾ inch) between them at the back of the cart (check the position against the side view in Fig. 9-9). You should be able to clamp on the axle plates so the long inside one goes up and the short outside one hangs down to support the wheel's axle (Fig. 9-10). Try this out with a real wheel to be positive it will be able to turn without rubbing

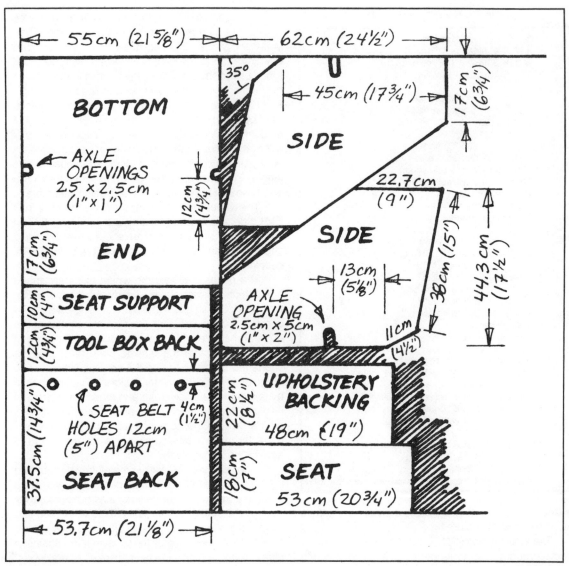

Fig. 9-3. Plywood cutting details.

somewhere. Notice how the wheel has to be tipped quite a bit for it to slip into the axle slots. In order to allow the wheels to be installed easily once the box is attached, hacksaw 1cm (⅜ inch) off the *inside* end of each wheel's axle bolt. Then try on the box to check that the cutouts on the side of the box are going to slip down over the axle ends correctly.

If you're welding or brazing, remember to clean the joints with a steel brush afterward and paint them to prevent rusting. If you're bolting, use ¼-inch × 2-inch bolts to secure the wheel housing to the inner frame, and two ¼ × 1½-inch bolts horizontally through each of the four axle plates to attach them (Fig. 9-11).

With the frame assembled and the wheels installed, the box can now be mounted in place. Attach it with four 1-inch sheet metal screws set in 3-mm (⅛-inch) holes drilled through the box and into the frame (on a bolted frame, use 1¼-inch screws to allow clearance of the bolt heads). Washers under the screws help protect the plywood. You can connect the

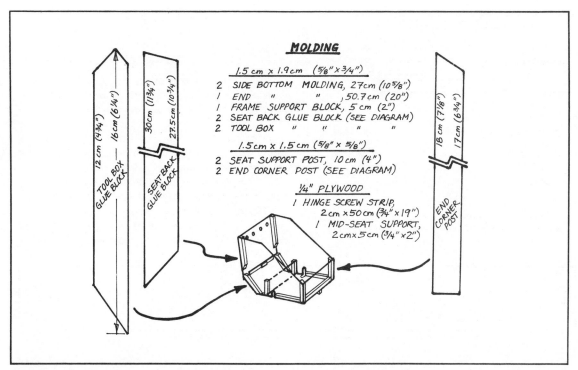

MOLDING

1.5 cm × 1.9 cm (5/8" × 3/4")

2 SIDE BOTTOM MOLDING, 27cm (10 5/8")
1 END   "   , 50.7cm (20")
1 FRAME SUPPORT BLOCK, 5 cm (2")
2 SEAT BACK GLUE BLOCK (SEE DIAGRAM)
2 TOOL BOX   "   "   "   "

1.5 cm × 1.5 cm (5/8" × 5/8")

2 SEAT SUPPORT POST, 10 cm (4")
2 END CORNER POST (SEE DIAGRAM)

1/4" PLYWOOD

1 HINGE SCREW STRIP,
   2 cm × 50 cm (3/4" × 19")
1 MID-SEAT SUPPORT,
   2 cm × 5 cm (3/4" × 2")

Labels on left piece: 12 cm (4 3/4") — 16 cm (6 1/4") — TOOL BOX GLUE BLOCK

Labels on middle piece: 30cm (11 3/4") — 27.5cm (10 3/4") — SEAT BACK GLUE BLOCK

Labels on right piece: 18 cm (7 1/8") — 17 cm (6 3/4") — END CORNER POST

Fig. 9-4. Molding details.

Fig. 9-5. A lightweight box, built of plywood and braced by molding at the joints, is glued and screwed together.

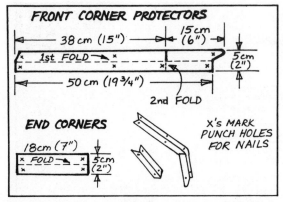

FRONT CORNER PROTECTORS

38 cm (15") 15 cm (6")

1st FOLD → 5 cm (2")

50 cm (19¾")

2nd FOLD

END CORNERS

18 cm (7")

× FOLD → 5 cm (2")

X's MARK PUNCH HOLES FOR NAILS

Fig. 9-6. Cut corner protectors from sheet metal scraps with tin snips; fold them by clamping them between boards in a vise.

cart to your bike with a rubber hitch, as shown in Chapter 4.

SEAT BELTS

Small children can wriggle out of any kind of seat belt short of a cross-chest harness. This kind of rigging includes straps over each shoulder and a third connecting strap that comes up between the legs and snaps to secure the harness. For children under the age of two, this belt arrangement keeps them sitting upright—even if they fall asleep while riding (Fig. 9-12). The harness keeps older kids from jumping around and getting into mischief.

Figure 9-13 shows a simple cross-chest system for either one or two children. Two kids can sit side by side with the shoulder straps looped through the holes

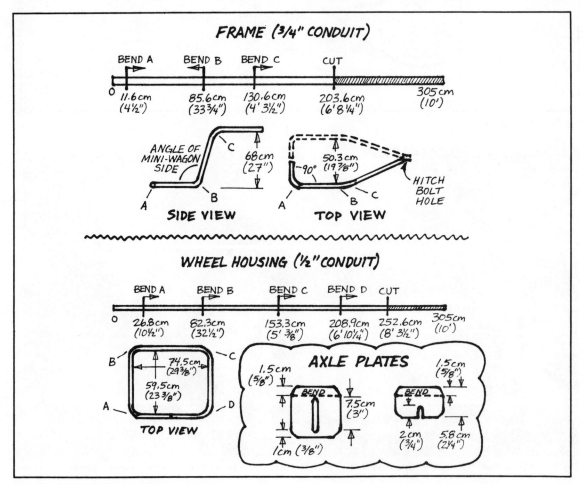

Fig. 9-7. Frame bending details.

Fig. 9-8. Plates to hold the wheels' axles are cut from electrical box covers. From left to right, the plates as bought, with edges clipped, holes drilled, slots cut, and bends completed.

above the seat. One child should ride in the middle for balance; move the shoulder straps to the center holes for him. Note that the bottom straps are fastened through grommets to the inside of the cart's toolbox, using short stove bolts or pop rivets.

TOP

A simple, lightweight top guarantees that you can get the kids to day-care on time, even in the rain. It provides a welcome shade on really sunny days. Because the top is open in front and back, you can keep an eye on the passengers. They get a good view out the back (Fig. 9-14).

The top is just two metal hoops and a piece of waterproof cloth with drawstrings sewn into the ends. Make the hoops from ⅛-inch × 1-inch aluminum bar (or steel, although it's heavier and must be painted). It can be bought at hardware stores or metal suppliers. Cut one length 152 cm (5 feet) and one 96 cm (38 inches). Drill holes for stove bolts 1 cm and 9 cm (½ inch and 3½ inches) from each end. Bend the bars into hoops by wrapping them around the metal rim of a

20-inch bicycle wheel. The short hoop will also need sharper bends 10 cm (4 inches) from either end (Fig. 9-15). Drill bolt holes 1 cm (½ inch) down from each of the upper corners of the cart and bolt the hoops temporarily in place. Adjust the hoops so their tops angle

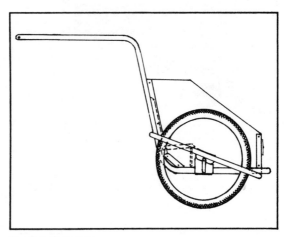

Fig. 9-9. Side view.

63

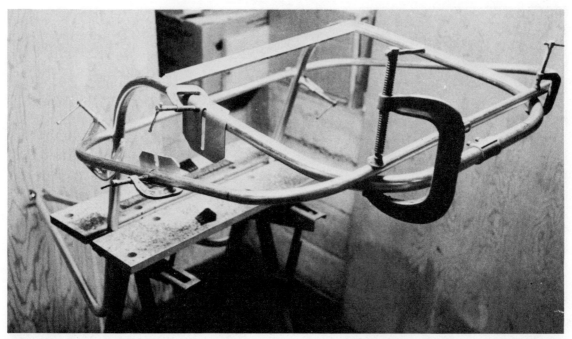

Fig. 9-10. The frame, ready for welding (here clamped upside down), should be checked to make sure the wheels will go on straight and the box will fit.

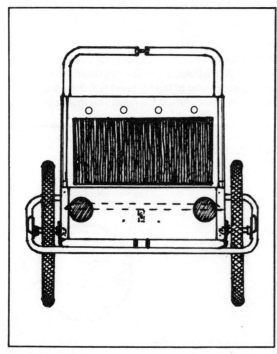

Fig. 9-11. End view.

Fig. 9-12. Youngsters are held securely with a cross-chest harness, even if they cannot sit up well by themselves or if they fall asleep during the trip.

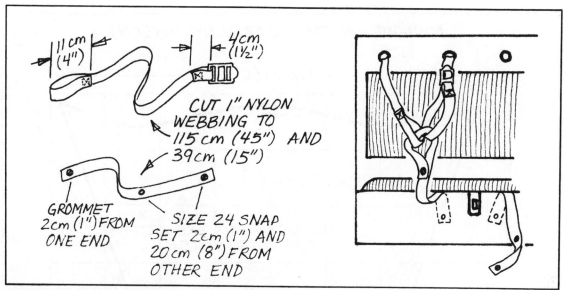

Fig. 9-13. Cross-chest seat belt harness details.

Fig. 9-14. The view's fine out the back. Mom can keep an eye on riders through a smaller opening in front.

out a bit and are just 74 cm (29 inches) apart. Drill the remaining four bolt holes through the cart sides and tighten on the fasteners. Use flat washers to protect the plywood and lock washers to keep the nuts tight.

Cut the top as shown in Fig. 9-16 from brightly colored nylon cloth and sear the edges with a candle flame. Hem the sides with a 3-cm (1⅛-inch) seam.

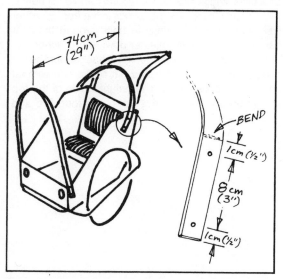

Fig. 9-15. Hoops for an optional covered wagon top can be easily bent and bolted to the cart. They also act as roll bars to protect young passengers.

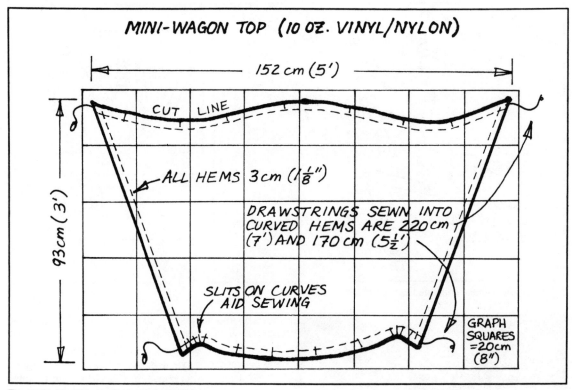

MINI-WAGON TOP (10 OZ. VINYL/NYLON)

152 cm (5')

93 cm (3')

CUT LINE

ALL HEMS 3 cm (1⅛")

DRAWSTRINGS SEWN INTO CURVED HEMS ARE 220 cm (7') AND 170 cm (5½')

SLITS ON CURVES AID SEWING

GRAPH SQUARES = 20 cm (8")

Fig. 9-16. Mini-Wagon top cutting details.

Sew drawstrings into the curved front and back hems.

Try on the top. Tie the strings in the front together first, then loop the strings in back around the rear bumper and tie them together down there. When everything is tightened, the opening in back should be big enough to lift the kids in and out of the cart without untying the drawstrings. The height inside of the top should be just right for kids up to age four; five and six-year-olds will prefer a top that's modified to be 8 cm (3 inches) taller.

With or without the top, the Mini-Wagon is proof that bigger is not necessarily better, especially when the load is smaller but precious. Parents will find this cart a vast improvement over lugging kids around in strollers and backpacks. Kids agree that there's hardly a more pleasant way to travel.

Chapter 10

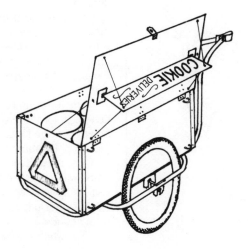

Booth

NOT EVERY NEW BUSINESS CAN AFFORD TO OPEN with a fleet of trucks and a big store in the high-rent district, and not every new business *wants* to. Sometimes a simpler, smaller scale is more efficient and pleasant.

This Booth is an ideal way for the small businessman to test out the market without committing himself to a huge investment—and without the hassles of a big operation (Fig. 10-1). With its locking lid and eye-catching signboard, it makes a first-rate delivery cart, too. There is plenty of room for parcels, mail, groceries, baked goods, flowers, or meals for shut-ins. The cart will hold 30 1-gallon cans with the lid closed.

A good-sized load is pretty easy to pull with almost any bike. If the cart's equipped with heavy-duty wheels and the load approaches 100 kg (222 pounds), you will want good brakes for stops and a low gear for starts. Once it's rolling, you can cruise in *high gear.*

A few poles and a canvas top turn the delivery cart into a booth for flea markets or crafts fairs (Fig. 10-2). There is room for layers of pottery, hand-sewn clothes, artwork, antiques, folding chairs, and trays. With the canvas awning rolled up and strapped on top, the business is ready to roll (Fig. 10-3). It only takes you 15

minutes to put up the top by yourself. Then you can set out the wares and sit back. You are protected from the sun or rain and secure against anything short of gale winds.

BIKE CART

The bike cart part of the Booth is not really more difficult or expensive to build than the Freighter. It's just a little larger (Table 10-1).

Cut plywood and molding as described in Fig. 10-4 for the box. Assemble it as for the Freighter. Before painting, take a look at how the signboard will be tied onto the lid. It will make room for advertising and stiffen the lightweight ¼-inch plywood of the top. Staple or tack the two little plywood positioners on the lid. Their little slots should hold the bottom corners of the signboard snugly.

Paint the wood parts. When they are dry, make sheet metal protectors for the corners (these are described in Chapter 4, but make them 10 cm or 4 inches longer for this cart). Put on the lid with three hinges and a hasp. Because the plywood is too thin for screws, fasten all this hardware with ½-inch stove bolts or pop rivets.

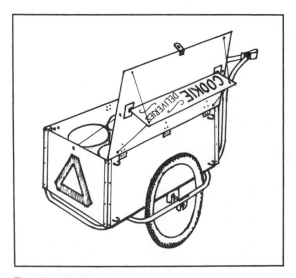

Fig. 10-1. The Booth.

Next you'll need some strings to keep the lid from falling backwards when it's opened. Use ⅛-inch nylon cord through little holes in the lid and cart end. Tie knots on the cord ends to keep them from pulling through the holes. The signboard also gets tied down with strings, as in the picture. The cord must be knotted on *both sides* of the signboard to keep it upright. Finally, don't forget a reflector or two for the back of the cart.

The frame and axle plates are bent and welded or bolted as for the Freighter. To make the frame long enough for the longer box, use the measurements in Fig. 10-5. Be sure to center the wheel housing on the frame so the cart will be balanced. Mount the box to the frame with sheet metal screws and washers. Put on a pair of 20-inch wheels. Use heavy motocross-type bicycle wheels if you anticipate loads of over 100 kg (222 pounds).

The whole cart won't take more than a weekend to

Fig. 10-2. This delivery cart converts to a market booth in about 15 minutes—without tools, as all the bolts have wing nuts.

Table 10-1. Booth Materials.

Lumber
1 4′ × 8′ sheet exterior ¼″ plywood
18′ 1 × 1 molding

Bike Shop
2 20″ × 1.75 front wheels

Hardware
3 10′ lengths of ¾″ EMT pipe
2 ¾″ EMT couplings
4 4″ × 4″ square electrical box
    covers (without "knockouts")
4 washers (for wheel axles)
3 hinges
1 hasp
about 24 ½″ stove bolts or pop rivets
10′ of ⅛″ nylon cord
some scraps of 26-gauge sheet metal
some ¾″ wood screws and short nails
4 1″ sheet metal screws with washers
tire sidewall or neoprene (for hitch)
1 ¼″ × 2″ bolt with wing nut

Additional for Bolted Frame
4 ¼″ × 2″ bolts
8 ¼″ × 1½″ bolts
4 1¼″ sheet metal screws with washers

Additional for Booth Awning
4 10′ lengths of ¾″ EMT pipe
1 10′ length of ½″ EMT pipe (for ridgepole)
6 ¼″ × 2½″ bolts with wing nuts
4 8′ lengths of 1 × 2 lumber
8 U-bolts (for ¾″ pipe)
1 7′ × 9′ canvas tarp
4 ⅜″ grommets
some staples or tacks

build, unless you've got some fancy painting scheme in mind. Hook it up to a bicycle, and that's really all you need to start a delivery business or a recycling service.

DELIVERY CART TO BOOTH

Once the cart's been used to haul wares to the open-air market, it can become the foundation for the market booth itself. The cover is designed to fit comfortably in a standard 8-foot-square market space. One person can set it up and take it down. There's room in front for customers. Because the cart's lid can still be locked, there's a safe place to keep personal belongings or extra wares.

The awning consists of a 7-foot × 9-foot (214-cm × 274-cm) sheet of canvas hemmed on all sides (Fig. 10-6). I found it was easiest to let a tent and awning store make one of these, because a standard sewing machine can't handle the heavy canvas needed to make the top tough and waterproof. The canvas store can also set two ⅜-inch grommets on each of the short sides, centered 88 cm (34 ¾ inches) apart, or you can do this yourself with an inexpensive grommet-setting tool and a hammer.

The framework supporting the awning rests on four poles that can be mounted to the cart by sliding each one down through two U-bolts fastened to the sides of the cart. Be sure to set the U-bolts so they are centered 88 cm (34¾ inches) apart. Don't make them so tight that the poles will ruin the cart's paint job when you slide them into place.

The front two poles are just 230-cm (7-foot, 6-inch) lengths of ¾-inch electrical conduit. Pound their upper ends flat so they can fit in slots in the 214-cm (7-foot) ridge pipe. These slots should be centered 88 cm (34¾ inches) apart. They can be made by drilling several small holes and pounding out the remaining material with a cold chisel.

Once the front two poles are in place, the cart should stand up by itself. The back two poles go on next. Bend them as shown in Fig. 10-5, pound their curved ends flat, and drill an 8-mm (5/16-inch) hole near this end to bolt the awning onto later.

The rest of the awning support framework is made of four pieces of 1 × 2 lumber. Cut two of these pieces to 235 cm (7 feet 8 inches) and taper their ends as shown in Fig. 10-7. Drill 8-mm (5/16-inch) holes vertically through both ends, 2.5 cm (1 inch) in from the tip. Bolt these long boards to the curved back poles. Mark where they cross the tall front poles, drill 8-mm (5/16-

Fig. 10-3. Packed up again for the road, the awning and poles ride atop the cart. The signboard keeps the lid flat and is a great way to advertise goods or services.

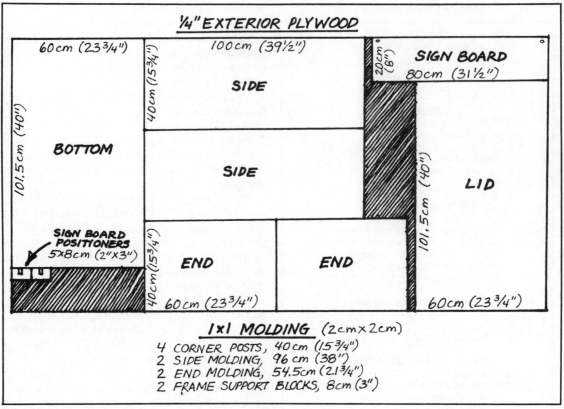

¼" EXTERIOR PLYWOOD

60cm (23¾")

100cm (39½")

SIGN BOARD
80cm (31½")

20cm (8")

40cm (15¾")

SIDE

101.5cm (40")

BOTTOM

SIDE

101.5cm (40")

LID

SIGN BOARD POSITIONERS
5×8cm (2"×3")

40cm (15¾")

END

END

60cm (23¾")

60cm (23¾")

1×1 MOLDING (2cm×2cm)

4 CORNER POSTS, 40cm (15¾")
2 SIDE MOLDING, 96cm (38")
2 END MOLDING, 54.5cm (21¾")
2 FRAME SUPPORT BLOCKS, 8cm (3")

Fgi. 10-4. Lumber cutting details.

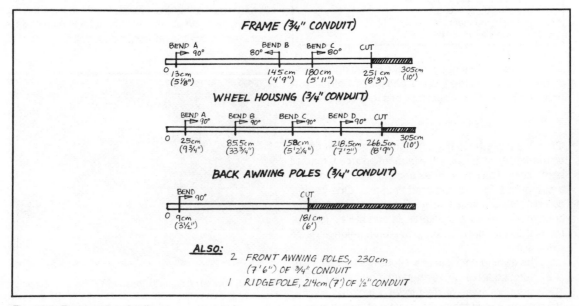

FRAME (¾" CONDUIT)

BEND A 90°   BEND B 80°   BEND C 80°   CUT

0   13cm (5⅛")   145cm (4'9")   180cm (5'11")   251cm (8'3")   305cm (10')

WHEEL HOUSING (¾" CONDUIT)

BEND A 90°   BEND B 90°   BEND C 90°   BEND D 90°   CUT

0   25cm (9¾")   85.5cm (33¾")   158cm (5'2¼")   218.5cm (7'2")   266.5cm (8'9")   305cm (10')

BACK AWNING POLES (¾" CONDUIT)

BEND 90°   CUT

0   9cm (3½")   181cm (6')

ALSO:

2 FRONT AWNING POLES, 230cm (7'6") OF ¾" CONDUIT
1 RIDGEPOLE, 214cm (7') OF ½" CONDUIT

Fig. 10-5. Pipe bending details.

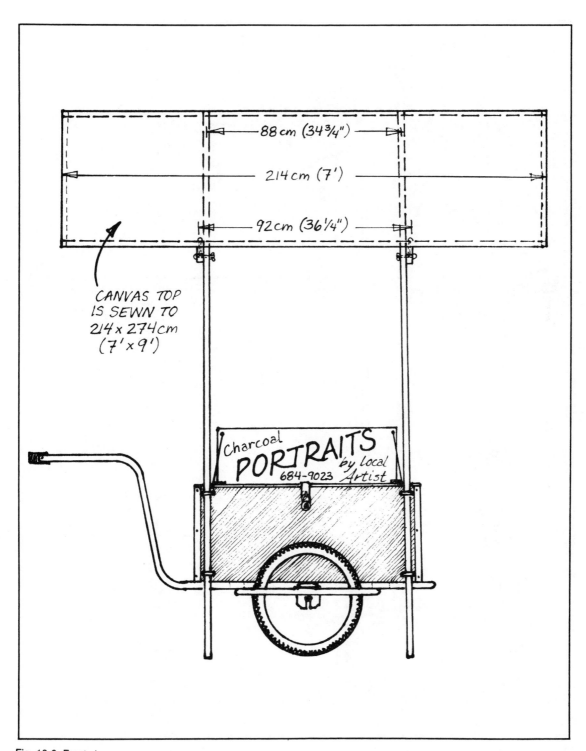

88 cm (34¾")

214 cm (7')

92 cm (36¼")

CANVAS TOP
IS SEWN TO
214 x 274 cm
(7' x 9')

Charcoal
PORTRAITS
684-9023 by local
Artist

Fig. 10-6. Front view.

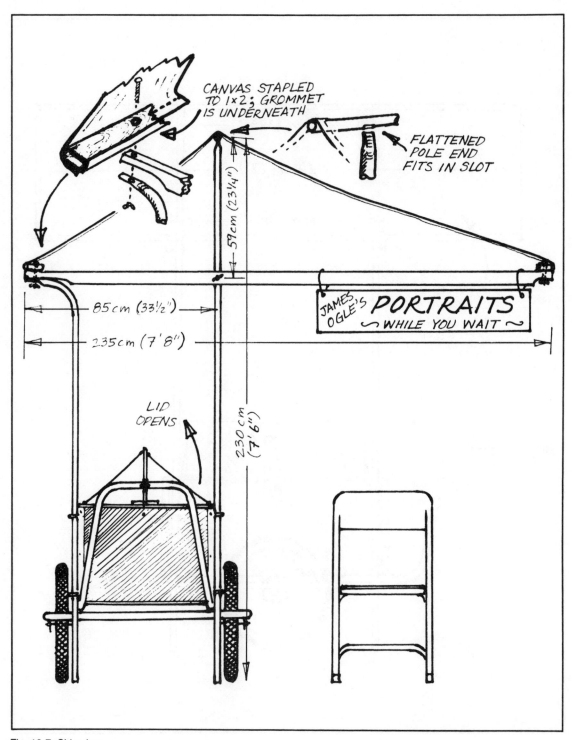

CANVAS STAPLED TO 1×2; GROMMET IS UNDERNEATH

FLATTENED POLE END FITS IN SLOT

59 cm (23¼")

JAMES OGLE'S **PORTRAITS** ~ WHILE YOU WAIT ~

85 cm (33½")

235 cm (7'8")

LID OPENS

230 cm (7'6")

Fig. 10-7. Side view.

inch) holes through them *and* the poles at the mark, and bolt them together there. If you use wing nuts on the bolts, you won't need tools to set up the Booth.

Only the awning remains. The canvas will need boards along the short edges to act as stiffeners. Staple or tack the canvas to 214-cm (7-foot) 1 × 2s along these edges. Make sure the two grommets in the hems are right in the middle of the 1 × 2s. Drill for bolts through the four grommet holes and through the stiffeners. Now the awning is ready to go up. Bolt it in place as shown in Fig. 10-7. If it isn't tight enough, drill lower bolt holes in the front support poles and reattach the lengthwise 1 × 2 braces there.

To pack up the awning, roll up the poles and lumber in the canvas, tie it with cords, and secure it onto the top of the cart. A little bag for the bolts and wing nuts keeps them from getting lost.

The Booth is useful for small businesses that need to reach the public but have to keep their costs down.

Chapter 11

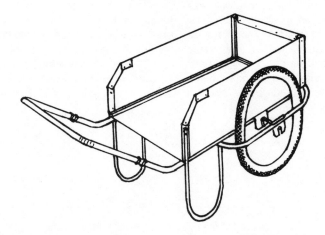

Steel-Frame Garden Cart

THIS CART CAN EASILY TAKE 300 POUNDS OF firewood across a field in a single load (Figs. 11-1 and 11-2). It only takes *one hand* to move even enormous loads. All of the weight is balanced over the two wheels—not on your arms and back (Fig. 11-3).

There seem to be jobs for a strong garden cart during every season of the year. In spring peat moss and compost are needed for the garden. A summer building project might mean hauling lumber, concrete block, or foundation rock. Bushels of apples and squash need to be moved in the fall and winter means more firewood for the shed.

Got an awkward load like a ladder or picnic table? Tie it down to the bumpers and off it goes. Need to take it down a steep hill? Simply push down on the handle and the two struts will drag, acting as brakes.

The garden cart handle can be removed in a few seconds and replaced with a *bike cart hitch* (Fig. 11-4). The garden cart then becomes a trailer for pulling bundled newspapers, garbage cans, or groceries behind a bicycle (Fig. 11-5).

There's no trick to building this cart. A borrowed pipe bender will turn electrical conduit into the frame. A screwdriver and a saw are needed to build the box. See Table 11-1.

BOX

Cut ¼-inch exterior plywood and 1 × 1 molding for the box as shown in Fig. 11-6. This will make a very strong box that's still light enough to be easy to push around. Although the box will be big enough for huge loads, it's narrow enough to fit through gates.

Attach the side moldings and corner posts to the cart sides with glue and ¾-inch or 1-inch screws, set in predrilled holes in the plywood. Put the end molding on the end and attach this assembly to the cart sides. Turn it upside down and glue and screw the bottom in place. Center the frame support block under the bottom, 25 cm (10-inches) from the front, where it will rest on the frame.

After sanding the wood parts, stain them all brown to preserve the wood and not show the dirt (Fig. 11-7). While the wood parts are drying, clip out some sheet metal that will strengthen the cart by protecting the plywood edges and corners.

Most sheet metal shops will sell scraps of 26-gauge stock by the pound. If you have tin snips and a vise, you can fashion these scraps into some fine edge protectors. Snip them as shown in Fig. 11-8. To fold them lengthwise so they'll just fit around a ¼-inch

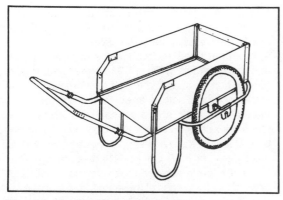

Fig. 11-1. The Steel-Frame Garden Cart.

plywood edge, clamp them in a vise between a 1 × 3 board and a long scrap of plywood. Use your palm to bend the sheet metal over the plywood into a U-shape. Unclamp them and bend the front edge protectors by hand to match the 45-degree angle on the cart's front. Put them in place and attach them with ⅜-inch pop rivets or stove bolts, set in holes drilled as shown in Fig. 11-8.

Finish up the box by adding two sheet metal protectors for the rear corners. Instructions for making these are in Chapter 4.

FRAME

There aren't any difficult bends in the garden cart

Fig. 11-2. A garden cart with large wheels rolls easily even with heavy loads or over uneven ground. This cart's metal frame makes it almost indestructible.

Fig. 11-3. The cart tips up for convenient dumping or loading of heavy objects.

frame. You'll need some electrical conduit and an electrician's pipe bender (either borrow one or buy one in a hardware store for under $20).

Set out three 10-foot lengths of ¾-inch conduit and mark them as in Fig. 11-9 for the inner frame, the garden cart handle, and the wheel housing. To bend the inner frame, set the arrow on the pipe bender on the mark for bend A (the *second* mark on the pipe). Make a 90-degree curve there. Do the same for bend B. You should have a U-shaped piece of conduit with the sides just 53.5 cm (21⅛ inches) apart. Cut a spacer bar out of scrap wood to just that length. Put it between the two sides of the inner frame to make sure that dimension is right—and stays right until the frame is welded or bolted. Make bends C and D to a 45-degree angle off the floor and cut the pipe as marked.

The garden cart handle is simply a short U-shaped piece of conduit. Once it's bent and cut, attach it to the inner frame with two of the outdoor-type ¾-inch EMT couplings. These connectors can be tightened with a wrench or by hand. They'll allow the handle to come off easily for storage or to attach a bike cart hitch later.

The wheel housing is a rectangle made with four

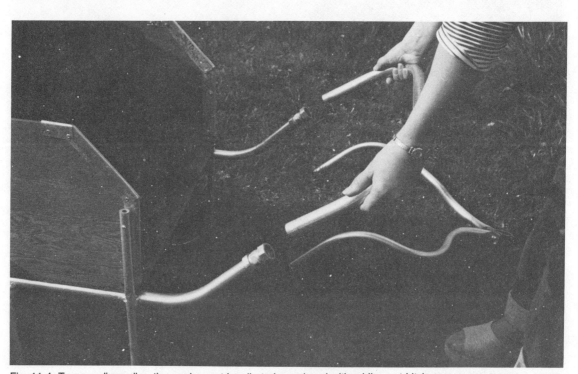

Fig. 11-4. Two couplings allow the garden cart handle to be replaced with a bike cart hitch.

Fig. 11-5. Loads can be transported across town by bike as well as around the yard.

90-degree bends. Join the ends with another ¾-inch coupling. Then clamp the wheel housing to the bottom of the inner frame. Put the long side of the wheel housing (the side without the coupling) at the back. Position it exactly underneath the pipe at the back of the inner frame. Check that the gaps for the wheels are close to 9.5 cm (3¾-inches) on either side.

    The two struts will attach to the wheel housing in back and to the frame in front. They will be bolted to the box on top to give the cart's sides some support. Bend them out of ½-inch conduit. Move the pipe bender to make a 180-degree curve.

    If you would rather use ¾-inch pipe here, remember that the curve will be slower, so more pipe will be needed. The back end will also have to attach to the frame closer to the wheels.

    If you're welding or brazing the frame, grind a curve in the end of the strut where it will butt up against the wheel housing. The edge of a grinding wheel will do the job. If it's to be bolted on, cut the strut 4 cm (1½ inches) longer, pound the end flat, bend it over, drill a ¼-inch hole, and secure it with the same bolt that holds the frame and wheel housing together.

    If you're running short of clamps, weld or bolt things in place before adding axle plates. Check that

Table 11-1. Steel-Frame Garden Cart Materials.

Lumber
1 4′ × 8′ sheet of ¼″ exterior plywood
10′ of 1 × 1 molding

Bike Shop
2 20″ × 1.75 or 20″ × 2.25 front wheels

Hardware
3 10′ lengths of ¾″ EMT pipe
1 10′ length of ½″ EMT pipe
3 outdoor-type ¾″ EMT couplings
4 4″ × 4″ square electrical box covers
    (without "knockouts")
7′ of 2½″-wide 26 gauge sheet metal
2 ¾″ faucet washers (to plug pipe
    ends in struts)
4 washers (for wheel axles)
12 ⅜″ pop rivets or stove bolts
4 1½″ stove bolts with washers
some ¾″ or 1″ wood screws
some short nails

Bolted Frame
6 ¼″ × 2″ bolts
8 ¼″ × 1½″ bolts

Bike Cart Hitch
1 ¼″ × 2″ bolt with wing nut
strip of tire sidewall or neoprene

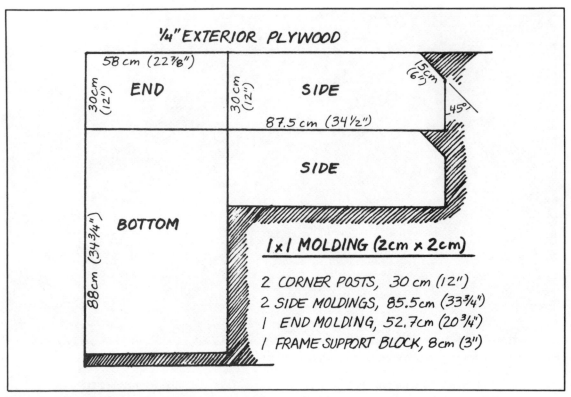

¼" EXTERIOR PLYWOOD

58 cm (22⅞")

END — 30 cm (12")

SIDE — 30 cm (12"), 87.5 cm (34½")

15 cm (6") 45°

SIDE

BOTTOM — 88 cm (34¾")

1 x 1 MOLDING (2cm x 2cm)

2 CORNER POSTS, 30 cm (12")
2 SIDE MOLDINGS, 85.5 cm (33¾")
1 END MOLDING, 52.7 cm (20¾")
1 FRAME SUPPORT BLOCK, 8 cm (3")

Fig. 11-6. Lumber cutting details.

Fig. 11-7. A coat of oil stain keeps the cart from showing dirt. Metal protectors on the front and back edges strengthen the plywood.

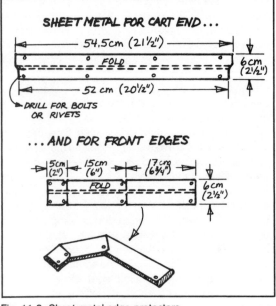

SHEET METAL FOR CART END . . .

54.5 cm (21½")
FOLD
6 cm (2½")
52 cm (20½")

DRILL FOR BOLTS OR RIVETS

. . . AND FOR FRONT EDGES

5 cm (2") 15 cm (6") 17 cm (6¾")
FOLD
6 cm (2½")

Fig. 11-8. Sheet metal edge protectors.

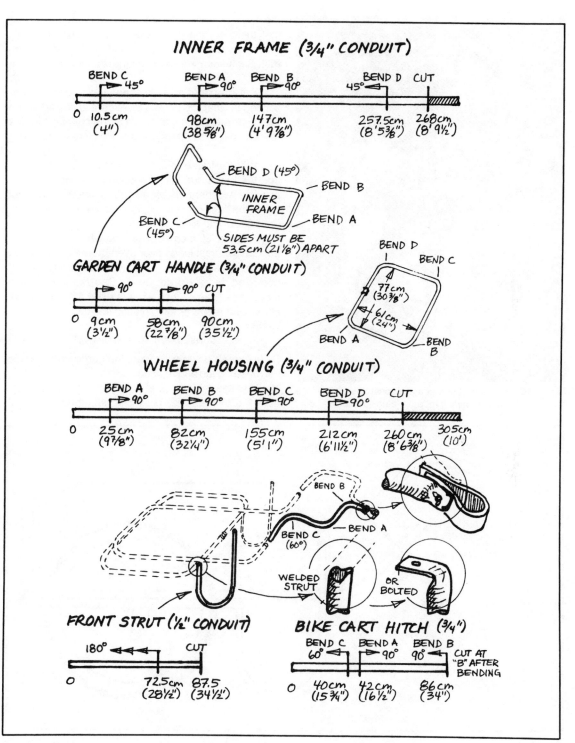

Fig. 11-9. Frame construction details.

Fig. 11-10. The second bend for the optional bike cart is more easily made with the pipe bender held upside down.

the cart's box will really fit between the struts first, and that there is room for the wheels. If you're welding, remember to paint all the joints afterwards to prevent rust. Six ¼-inch × 2-inch fasteners should do for bolting.

Put on plates to hold the wheel's axles as described in Chapter 4. Take extra care to line up all the axle slots exactly in the middle of the openings for the wheels, because there's not a lot of room for error there.

With the frame finished, you can put on the wheels and the box. Four 1½-inch stove bolts with washers and lock washers should keep the box in place. Put two in the back corners into the frame and two through the front of the sides into the struts.

Regular 20-inch front bicycle wheels are strong enough for most loads over even ground. You'll need heavier spokes and axles for that 300-pound load of firewood in a rutted field. Choose the heavy motocross-type 20-inch wheels used for kid's bikes, either with metal or thick plastic spokes.

CONVERSION TO A BIKE CART

By unscrewing two couplings, the garden cart handle can be removed and replaced with a bike cart hitch that *doubles* the usefulness of your cart. Newspaper carriers like this feature. They can haul their bundle of

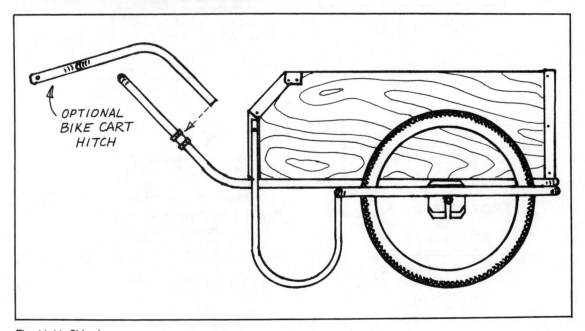

OPTIONAL
BIKE CART
HITCH

Fig. 11-11. Side view.

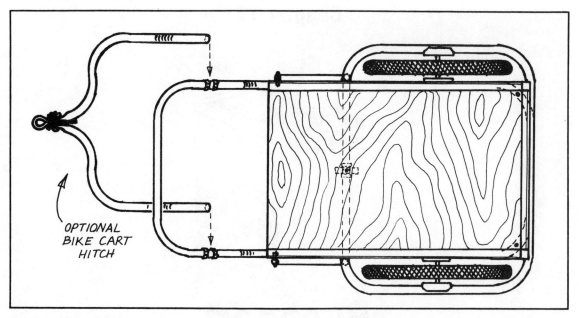

Fig. 11-12. Top view.

papers from the drop point to their routes, pulling their carts with bicycles. Then they unhitch the carts and walk them around the routes, carrying even the heaviest Sunday issues easily.

With the cart hooked into a bike's seat post, the cart is tipped back just enough that the struts in front have good clearance. It pulls and maneuvers as easily as any single-purpose bike cart would.

Use the ¾-inch pipe left over from making the garden cart handle to make the hitch. You'll need two hitch halves, each with three tricky bends. These are easier to make in a long pipe than a short one, so cut the pieces to length *after* each one is bent.

Mark for the three bends on one end of the pipe (Fig. 11-9). Then make bend A (the *middle* bend)—a simple 90-degree angle. Bend B is a 90-degree angle back *toward* A, resulting in an S-shaped curve. To get leverage for this bend, you'll need to turn the pipe bender upside down with the handle on the ground. Pull the pipe down over the tool while you brace the

handle with a knee (Fig. 11-10). Set the S-shaped curve flat on the floor for the final bend, then bend up to just 60 degrees. Because the pipe end will be short, you'll have to step hard on the bender to get leverage.

Cut off this first half of the hitch and make the second half as a mirror image of the first (in other words, make bend C with the pipe lying on its other side). Pound the ends of the pipes flat for the hitch (where you marked for bend B). Drill an 8-mm (5/16-inch) hole for the hitch bolt 2 cm (¾-inch) from the end. Where you pounded the pipe flat, there will be some sharp square corners that need to be bent aside before you can add a rubber hitch (as in Chapter 3), with a ¼-inch × 2-inch bolt and wing nut. (See Figs. 11-11 and 11-12).

With the two interchangeable handles, this cart is so much more versatile than a wheelbarrow that it's hardly in the same class. You'll discover that this hybrid cart really can haul almost anything and go almost anywhere.

Chapter 12

Pushcart

MANY SMALL BUSINESSES HAVE STARTED OUT with pushcarts. There's no rent to pay, no need to hire employees, and no iron-clad nine-to-five schedule to keep. There's no need to pay for advertising, because a pushcart is its own advertisement (Fig. 12-1).

Suppose you want to be your own boss and you've got a few recipes that look promising—say, an apple pie that makes grown men beg for more or barbecued chicken that took first place at the fair. Your dream may be Martha's Pie Shoppe or Bob's Barbecued Chicken Inn, but the loan officer at the bank will want to see more than a recipe before he'll bankroll that dream.

You can test out the market inexpensively with a pushcart. When you've made a name for yourself and perhaps even expanded to a second cart, that same loan officer will be a lot friendlier when you talk with him about a more permanent home for your business.

THE PUSHCART BUSINESS

The very first step in the pushcart business—and sometimes the hardest—is getting a permit. The same city officials that try to make things easy for a new industry—regardless of the cost in tax incentives, land,

and environmental damage—will probably make it difficult for the new pushcart business despite evidence that small businesses create far more new jobs than industries. Ask at your city hall; sometimes permits are free.

With the permit in hand, it's time to look at the cart itself. From my experience, the entrepreneur who is determined to be a success in the pushcart business does not pinch pennies by building a shoddy cart. Customers often judge a vendor's wares by his cart, especially for frozen or hot foods that cannot be easily displayed.

Here are plans for a pushcart that's strictly top-of-the-line, both in appearance and efficiency. It has two top doors that open to a large box that can be insulated. Underneath, two smaller side doors provide access to a second storage area suitable for stashing paper cups, napkins, a money box, or a folding chair (Fig. 12-2).

Two strong wheelchair casters in front allow the cart to turn easily, while the bulk of the weight rests on a pair of motocross-type 20-inch bicycle wheels (Fig. 12-3). The wheels can handle a load of 150 kg (333 pounds). The cart weighs 40 kg (89 pounds) without a load or 50 kg (111 pounds) with the canopy.

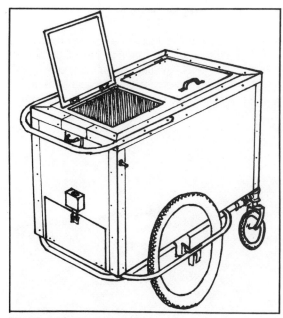

Fig. 12-1. The Pushcart.

The canopy is designed to be stable enough to stay up while the cart rolls from place to place. It provides protection from rain squalls and casts enough shade to keep the cart cool in the sun. You can put up the canopy alone. When it's time to head home, the canopy rolls into a 183-cm (6-foot) bundle that can be tied atop the cart (Fig. 12-4).

With some pushcarts, taking the cart home can be the hardest part of the day. Massive carts of oak and brass may look nice on the street, but they have less appeal when you have to shove them up into a truck to haul them home. The pushcart in this chapter is light enough that it can easily by pulled to and from work with a bicycle. A simple bike hitch quickly attaches to a long threaded bolt mounted through the cart's front sides. The triangular arrangement of the bike hitch bars prevents the cart from swaying side to side but allows the hitch to pivot up or down, so you can go over bumps or up driveways.

Set aside about a week to build this cart, including time for the paint to dry. Materials should run about $200, largely because of the wheelchair casters, bike wheels, and canvas top (Table 12-1). The other materials are inexpensively available in retail stores. Although this is not a project for the complete beginner, an average handyman should have no trouble building it in a home shop. Because the frame cannot be bolted

together, it may be necessary to hire out about two hours of welding work.

PUSHCART BOX

You probably should build the box first. It will have to be painted nicely, and all those coats will take time to dry.

Cut molding and plywood to the sizes shown in Figs. 12-5 and 12-6. Then locate the two sides (they're not the same size as the inside shelf or the bottom). Glue and screw a total of four pieces of molding on each side—two corner posts, flush with the ends, and two side moldings, one flush with the bottom and one 18 cm (7⅛ inches) up from the bottom. When the molding is positioned correctly, mark for four to six screws per piece and drill holes for these fasteners in the plywood. Glue the pieces and screw them in place.

Attach a piece of shelf support molding to each end, also 18 cm (7⅛ inches) from the bottom, and evenly centered. The molding will cover up 1 cm (⅜ inch) of the door opening, so the little end doors will have something to close against. The sides and ends of the cart can be put together with glue and screws. The whole thing has to be turned upside down to attach the bottom.

The last piece of molding, a shelf support, should be positioned in the middle of the inside shelf and screwed in place before the shelf itself is lowered into the cart and attached. Once the shelf is in, a well-aimed long nail through the side will make sure that middle shelf support stays put.

The top is made of ½-inch plywood for extra strength. It will never be glued to the cart. Once the sheet metal trim is screwed on later, it will be on plenty tight. You will still be able to completely remove the top to clean out the inside of the cart or to install insulation.

The top doors are cut to be 1.5 cm (⅝ inch) wide on all sides than the holes they cover in the top. To make the doors fit down into the holes, cut a rabbet (a notch or ledge) to this width on each edge. Set a table saw to a depth of 5 mm (¼ inch), with the fence 1.5 cm (⅝ inch) from the blade. Cut the doors on all edges and chisel off the bottom two layers of the five-ply plywood. To make the doors look nice, bevel the top edges with a block plane and sand them round.

Now you're ready to paint the wood parts. Because some inside spaces are somewhat difficult to reach, I prefer to stain these areas (you only have to reach them with a brush once that way). Use a quality oil-base enamel paint for the outside, top, and the four doors. You'll need two coats of paint. When the parts are dry, add whatever lettering or art you want. Leave room for the wheels or fenders and a 4-cm (1½-inch) margin on all sides for the sheet metal trim (Fig. 12-7). To protect the paint job and make the cart easy to clean, finish with three coats of clear, glossy liquid plastic.

FRAME AND FOUR WHEELS

While the paint is drying, find some wheels and build a frame to fit them. Strangely enough, the 8-inch swivel casters for the front of the cart will probably cost more than the 20-inch motocross-type bicycle wheels in back. A pair of first-rate bike wheels with ⅜-inch axles

Fig. 12-2. Two top doors open to a large box that can be insulated for either hot or cold foods. A storage area underneath has room for paper cups, napkins, and a folding chair.

Fig. 12-3. The Pushcart rolls smoothly on 20-inch bicycle wheels and 8-inch wheelchair casters—even with the canopy up.

will cost around $50 fitted out with tires and tubes. They're worth the money, because the cheaper wheels with ¼-inch axles won't handle the weight of a pushcart. A pair of wheelchair casters, with forks and bearings, costs closer to $100, largely because of the staggering markup on medical equipment. Check at salvage centers and wheelchair repair shops for some used units that will work just as well on a pushcart. It's probably not a good idea to try and get by with cheaper, smaller casters, as they won't roll over bumps easily and are sure to break or bend loose. The

casters must be large and very strong, especially if the cart is ever to be pulled by a bicycle.

On a wheelchair the upright axle of a front caster bolts between two bearings into a special pipe. On a pushcart it can bolt into an ordinary pipe (Fig. 12-8). A short nipple of 1-inch iron pipe works well, even though the wheelchair bearings do not seat entirely inside this size opening. When the 1-inch nipple is tightly screwed into a 1-inch tee, the top of the tee should be pretty close to 32 cm (12½ inches) off the ground—the same height as the bottom of the cart. You may find that the lip on the upper bearing has to be ground off in order for the nipple to fit into the tee.

When the wheelchair casters are solidly attached to 1-inch plumbing pipe, you could build the entire frame out of iron pipe, but it would weigh a ton. To convert from 1-inch iron pipe to lighter ¾-inch electrical conduit, put a ¾-inch or 1-inch reducer bushing in the side opening of the 1-inch tee (leave the top opening free so a socket wrench can later tighten the wheelchair caster axle nut if necessary). Add a ¾-inch nipple and tee as in Fig. 12-9. You'll discover that ¾-inch EMT conduit fits perfectly into the ¾-inch tee—so well, in fact, that it can be threaded in just by twisting it with your hand.

Bend ¾-inch conduit for the rest of the frame. Mark and cut two 10-foot lengths as shown in Fig. 12-9 and bend them with an electrician's pipe bender. Set the arrow on the pipe bender on each mark and lower the handle until you've got a 90-degree curve. The wheel housing should have a square shape when its ends are connected with an EMT coupling. The frame should be U-shaped; screw the wheelchair caster assemblies onto these ends. Cut a 57-cm (22½-inch) length of conduit and insert its ends into the side openings of the ¾-inch tees. This should brace the frame apart to the correct width for the cart's box.

The frame needs one more brace to keep the casters from twisting and to give the box something onto which to bolt. This is made from ⅛-inch × 1-inch steel bar; you'll need about a 1-meter length (39½ inches). The brace can be bent by clamping it in a vise and pushing it over with your palm. You may have to make six bends to get it to fit as in Fig. 12-9, flush with the top of the 1-inch tees and touching the tees on the

Fig. 12-4. One person can take the canopy down in about 10 minutes. Then the cart can be hitched to a bicycle for a speedy trip home.

86

Table 12-1. Pushcart Materials.

Lumber Store
2 4' × 8' sheets of ¼" exterior plywood
½ 4' × 8' sheet of ½" exterior plywood
30' 1 × 1 molding
2 10' lengths of 1½" × 1½" galvanized sheet metal cap strip (for trim)

Plumbing Supply Store
2 1" nipples
2 1" tees
2 ¾"-1" reducer bushings
2 ¾" nipples
2 ¾" tees

Hardware
3 10' lengths of ¾" EMT conduit
1 ¾" EMT coupling
4 4" × 4" square electrical box covers (without "knockouts")
100 cm (39½") of ⅛" × 1" steel bar
8 brass hinges
2 cabinet clasps
2 small door handles
1 box ¾" wood screws
some short nails and wood glue
some ⅜" or ½" sheet metal screws
some ½" stove bolts or pop rivets
6 1½" sheet metal screws
6 2" stove bolts with washers and nuts

Bike Shop
2 20" × 1.75 front motocross-type bicycle wheels (with ⅜" axles)

Wheelchair Supply
2 8" front wheelchair casters, with forks and bearings

Additional for Canopy
1 6' × 6' canvas tarp
4 ⅜" grommets
2 large U-bolts
2 7 cm (3") blocks of 2 × 4 lumber
4 6' lengths of 1 × 2 lumber
2 10' lengths of ¾" EMT conduit
1 10' length of ½" EMT conduit
6 ¼" × 3" carriage bolts with wing nuts
10' of nylon cord
2 small cotter pins or eyebolts

Additional for Bike Hitch
1 10' length of ¾" EMT conduit
1 3' length of ¼" threaded bolt stock
4 ¼" nuts
10 ¼" washers
1 ¼" × 2" bolt
3 ¼" wing nuts
a strip of tire sidewall or neoprene
2 rear reflectors

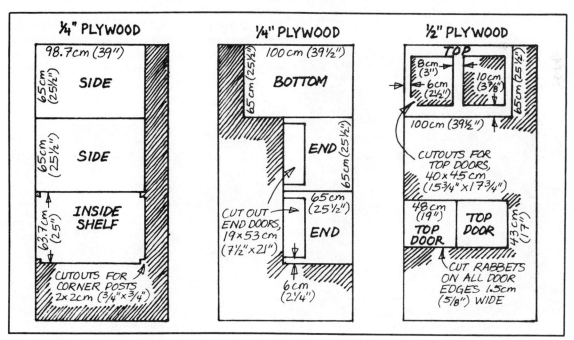

Fig. 12-5. Plywood cutting details.

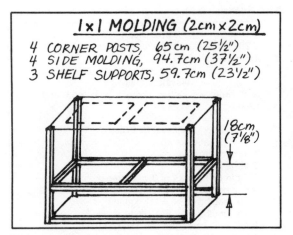

1×1 MOLDING (2cm × 2cm)

4 CORNER POSTS, 65cm (25½")
4 SIDE MOLDING, 94.7cm (37½")
3 SHELF SUPPORTS, 59.7cm (23½")

18cm (7⅛")

Fig. 12-6. Molding details.

sides. The ends of this bar should be welded down; the sides will be welded securely to the 1-inch tees. Two small holes drilled in the top of the brace will allow the box to be bolted on later.

All the frame needs now before welding are the axle plates for the 20-inch wheels. Make these as for the Freighter in Chapter 4. After you've satisfied yourself that the wheels will fit in their slots and be straight,

clamp and weld all the joints of the frame. I also weld the pipe fittings to keep them from turning, but do not weld the 1-inch nipple on the caster axles or the EMT coupling on the wheel housing.

After welding, remove the slag with a steel brush and paint the entire frame. Then you can mount the 20-inch wheels on the frame and try rolling it around. If the paint on the box is dry, you can put the box and frame together. Six 1½-inch stove bolts will hold them together—four through the wheel housing and two into the steel bar in front (Fig. 12-10).

FINISHING THE PUSHCART

The first step in finishing the cart is to cover up the ragged plywood corners with some attractive galvanized sheet metal trim. Two 10-foot lengths of 1½-inch × 1½-inch cap strip (used in roofing houses) will do. Tack 65-cm (25½-inch) lengths on each corner first. One 10-foot length of this metal is almost enough to go all the way around the cart's top (and thus hold the top on). By cutting 45-degree slits with tin snips, you can bend a single piece around the corners and back nearly to the start. A shorter piece underneath will make up the final few centimeters without being obtrusive. This trim can be fastened securely with very short panhead sheet metal screws, set in holes punched by a large nail.

Before the top is on, you may want to insulate the cart. Remember that heat rises but cold sinks, so a cart for hot foods will need extra insulation on the top. A cart for frozen foods may only need thin insulation on top but as much as 10 cm (4 inches) on the bottom. If you're selling dairy products, health officials may want

Fig. 12-7. Once the inside shelf is in place, the bottom can be installed. The top (in the background) attaches with sheet metal trim after the wood parts have been painted.

Fig. 12-8. Wheelchair casters mount solidly into standard-sized water pipe fittings.

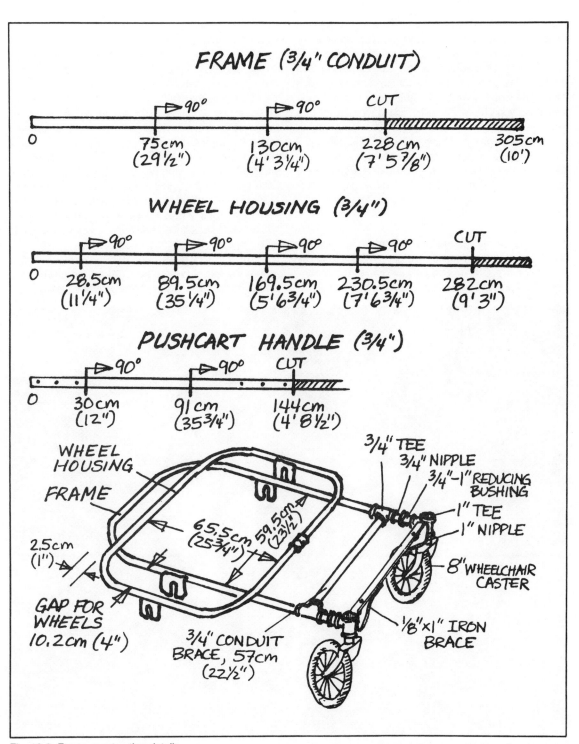

Fig. 12-9. Frame construction details.

the cart's box lined with a washable surface. A drain hole in the bottom for hosing out spills is probably wise.

Now the doors can go on. I use brass hinges all around, with big handles for the top doors and little cabinet clasps for the bottom ones. Screws for this hardware won't hold on the thin plywood in many cases, so you'll have to use ½-inch stove bolts or pop rivets.

Bend a handle as shown in Fig. 12-9 and attach it with 1½-inch panhead sheet metal screws—right into the ½-inch plywood cart top. If you think the cart needs fenders on the wheels (and they do look nice), directions for making these are in Chapter 7.

CANOPY

A canopy protects you from the weather and also acts like a banner above the crowd, letting people know where you are. Obtain a brightly-colored piece of canvas for a top. A tent and awning store can sew it for you

to a 6-foot-square finished size (Fig. 12-11). The canvas store can also set ⅜-inch grommets for you (or you can do it yourself with a tool that costs $2). Space two grommets 108 cm (42½ inches) apart in the middle of two opposite sides.

To make the frame supporting the canopy, first make some brackets to screw to the ends of the pushcart to support two poles. The top bracket consists of a large U-bolt fastened to the cart through a small piece of ¼-inch plywood. The lower bracket is a short length of 2 × 4 lumber with a 2.5-cm (1-inch) hole drilled partway through it. These brackets support two 172-cm (5-foot, 8-inch) poles made of ¾-inch conduit. Flatten the tops of these poles with a hammer so they can fit inside slots drilled and punched into a 183-cm (5 foot) ridgepole made of ½-inch conduit.

The canvas goes over this ridgepole, but first securely staple or tack 183-cm (6-foot) lengths of 1 × 2 lumber to opposite sides of the canvas to keep it stiff

Fig. 12-10. The welded frame bolts to the bottom of the cart.

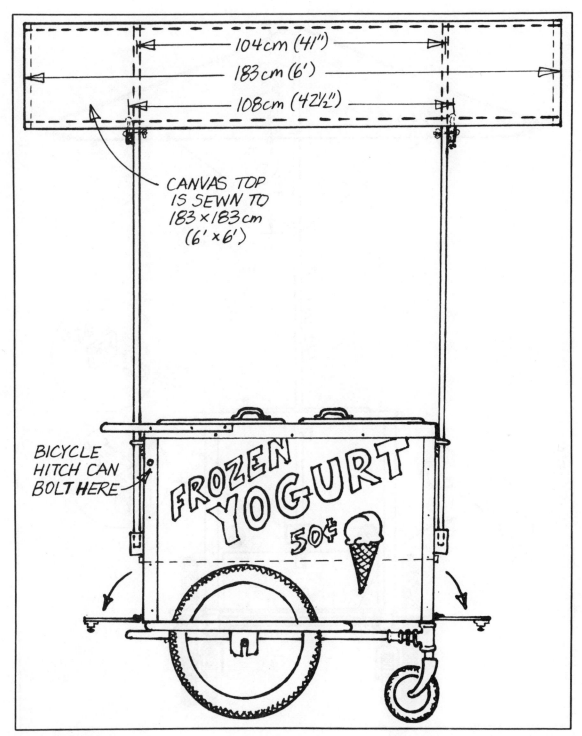

104cm (41")

183cm (6')

108cm (42½")

CANVAS TOP
IS SEWN TO
183 × 183 cm
(6' × 6')

BICYCLE
HITCH CAN
BOLT HERE

FROZEN YOGURT 50¢

Fig. 12-11. Side view.

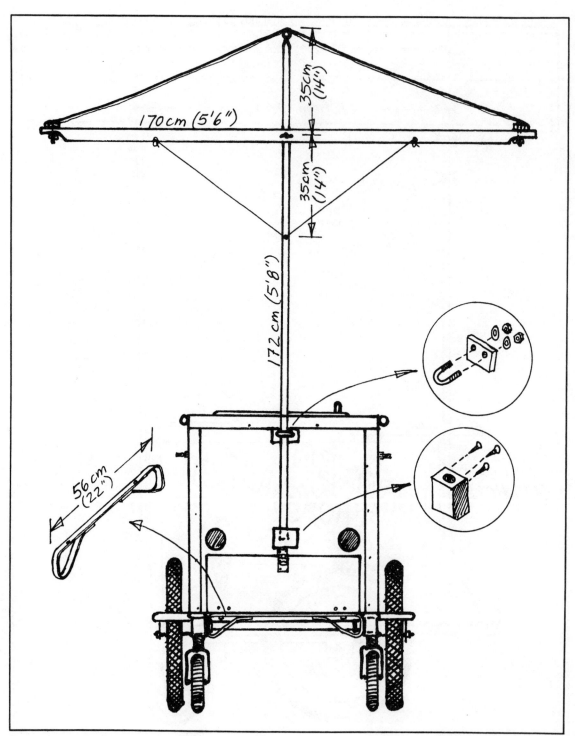

Fig. 12-12. End view.

and taut. You will have covered up the four grommets in the process, so drill through them and through the 1 × 2 stiffeners with an 8-mm (5/16-inch) bit.

Make two cross beams out of 1 × 2 lumber. Cut them to 170 cm (5 feet, 6 inches). Drill holes in the middles of these beams and, after tapering the ends to 1-inch (2 cm), drill holes vertically 6 cm (2¼ inches) from either end. To attach these boards to the poles with ¼-inch × 3-inch carriage bolts, you will have to first drill holes 35 cm (14 inches) from the top of the poles (a hammer and punch help start the holes). With the cross beams bolted on, the canvas can be thrown over the ridgepole and then attached to the cross beams with 3-inch carriage bolts through the grommet holes and the stiffeners. If you use wing nuts on all the bolts, the top can be assembled without any tools.

As a final touch to keep the canopy from slipping in the wind, tie nylon cords to holes in the cross beams (Fig. 12-12). Attach these cords to a cotter pin or small eyebolt that can be inserted into a small hole in the support pole.

HITCHING THE CART TO A BICYCLE

This light pushcart rolls so well that it can easily be towed home with a bike. The cart can be quickly moved through parks or on paths where motorized traffic is not allowed, and it can reach markets that other concessions can't touch.

You need a place on the cart itself to connect a hitch. Use a long, threaded ¼-inch bolt (hardware stores sell these in 3-foot lengths). Drill 7-mm (¼-inch) holes for the bolt in the front sides of the cart, 86 cm (33½ inches) from the ground—the average height of a bike's seat posts. Make sure the holes line up and

that they go through the sheet metal trim, the plywood side, and the 1 × 1 corner post inside. Then slide the bolt all the way through the cart, in one hole and out the other, and saw it off so it sticks out 4 cm (1½ inches) on either side. Thread on four nuts and washers and tighten them inside and out.

Make two bars that will connect the cart to a rubber hitch wrapped around the bike's seat post. These bars are simply ¾-inch conduit cut to 85 cm (33½ inches). Pound them flat at both ends (they will fit better if this is done at a slight angle). Drill 8-mm (5/16-inch) holes for the hitch bolts 2 cm (¾ inch) from either end. With a pair of pliers, bend the sharp front corners aside slightly before clamping the bars to the rubber connector wrapped around the seat post. For details on making and using the rubber connector, see Chapter 3. Use a ¼-inch × 2-inch bolt and wing nut to clamp this connector, then attach the other end of the bars to the cart's bolt ends with several washers and a wing nut.

Remember that your loaded cart will probably weigh 100 to 150 kg (200 to 300 pounds), so check your bike's brakes to be sure you can stop once you've started rolling. In wet weather you will want aluminum rims on the wheels so your brake pads will still grab on. Always gear down at intersections so you can start up when the light changes. Never ride at top speed (those casters in back aren't built for racing). Take bumps slowly and head-on.

A pushcart is a low-cost way to take your business to that ideal location. Once you're there, you can focus your attention on putting out the right product at the right price to win the repeat customers that are the heart of every pushcart market.

Chapter 13

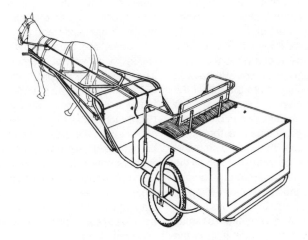

Pony Cart

A HORSE CAN PULL A MUCH BIGGER LOAD IN A CART than it can carry on its back. Hooking up a two-wheeled rig is probably the simplest way to make your horse more energy-efficient.

This cart is designed to do just that (Fig. 13-1). There's a large comfortable seat up front, but there's also plenty of room in back for loads for which you'd probably need a tractor or a pickup—things like six bales of hay, two trash cans, or a full load of kids (Fig. 13-2). Because the cart only weighs 45 kg (100 pounds), it's easy pulling for even a pleasure pony.

The cart can be built in about three days. Materials shouldn't cost more than $90, including about $50 for a pair of new motocross-type bicycle wheels (Table 13-1). The box is built of sturdy ½-inch plywood. The frame and shafts are welded together out of electrical conduit. Bending this pipe to the right shape will not be difficult with a little practice. Dimensions are given to adapt the cart to either a pony, Welsh pony, or horse.

BOX

To build this light but strong box, cut ½-inch plywood and 1 × 1 molding to the shapes shown in Fig. 13-3. You'll also need a couple other wooden parts for the

cart, and you should get them cut to size at the same time. The seat is an 87.5-cm (34½-inch) length of 1 × 12 lumber and the mudguard (which the singletree attaches to in front) is a 90-cm (35½-inch) piece of 1 × 8 lumber.

First mount the side molding and corner posts to the sides. Use 1-inch wood screws in predrilled holes to clamp the glue. The end molding goes on the end—centered at the bottom—before the end is mounted to the cart sides. The bottom is then glued and screwed in place. This makes a pretty strong box, but I add four ¼-inch × 1½-inch carriage bolts through the corner posts to make sure the sides and end stay together under heavy use.

There should be four little pieces of molding left. The two frame support blocks screw to the bottom of the cart where they will rest on the wheel housing and support the middle of the box. The two seat supports go on the inside of the sides, 2 cm (¾ inch) from the top and 25 cm (10 inches) from the front edge.

Finish the box with a coat of wood stain for the interior and the bottom (this will be easier to clean than paint), and a couple coats of paint for everything on the outside (don't forget the footrest and the mudguard). If

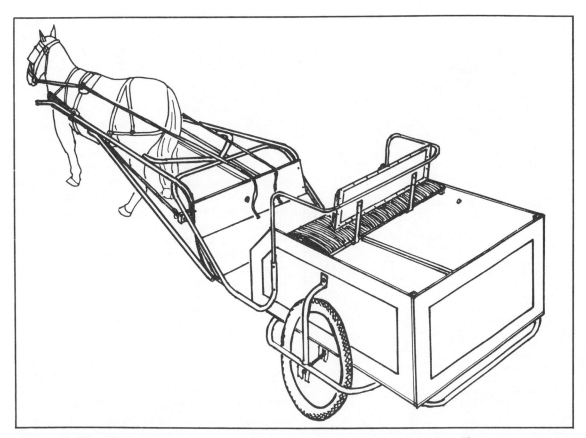

Fig. 13-1. The Pony Cart.

Fig. 13-2. With a padded seat and a large cargo area, the Pony Cart is well-suited to both light farm chores and pleasure rides.

Table 13-1. Pony Cart Materials.

Lumber
1½ 4' × 8' sheets of ½" exterior plywood
3' of 1 × 8 lumber
3' of 1 × 12 lumber
3' of 2 × 4 lumber
17' of 1 × 1 molding

Bike Shop
2 20" × 1.75 motocross-type front bicycle wheels
    (with ⅜" axles)

Fabric
1" foam rubber (for padding seat)
vinyl upholstery fabric

Hardware
7 10' lengths of ¾" EMT conduit
1 10' length of ½" EMT conduit
2 ¾" EMT couplings
4 4" × 4" square electrical box covers
    (without "knockouts")
1 box 1" wood screws
4 1½" wood screws
6 ¼" × 1½" carriage bolts
10 2" stove bolts with washers
2 U-bolts
4 heavy ⅜" eyebolts
5' of ⅛" × 1" strap iron
some ½" panhead screws
2 lbs. of 3/32" #6011 welding rod

you'd like to add some striping, now's the time. A few final coats of liquid plastic or fiberglass will protect your artwork and keep the outside easy to clean, too.

BENDING ELECTRICAL CONDUIT

Using ¾-inch electrical conduit for the cart's chassis has several advantages: it's light, pregalvanized, and easily bent to shape with an electrician's pipe bender. Where extra strength is needed, extra pieces used as braces will do the job. Although the cart only requires seven 10-foot lengths of this pipe, it usually comes in bundles of 10. I would recommend getting a whole bundle if you haven't ever tried bending pipe before—just to put you under less pressure to get it perfect the first try.

Mark the frame and wheel housing pipes as shown in Fig. 13-4. Set the arrow on the pipe bender on the first mark for the frame. Lower the tool's handle until the short end of the pipe has bent up exactly 90 degrees. Move the tool to the next mark and make another right angle. The frame should now be U-

shaped, with the two sides 84 cm (33 inches) apart. The wheel housing is easy to bend, because there are just four right-angle corners. It should come just short of making a square shape when finished. Finish the square by attaching a short 27-cm (10⅝-inch) piece of conduit between the two ends with two ¾-inch EMT couplings.

Lay out the frame on top of the wheel housing. There should be a 10-cm (4-inch) gap on either side for the wheels. To bolt the wheel axles on later, you'll need to position four axle plates in the middle of the wheel openings. Make these as described in Chapter 4. Weld all the joints except the EMT couplings, which shouldn't need it. Because this galvanized pipe gives off zinc oxide fumes when welded, work in a well-ventilated area and wear a filter-type respirator. To finish this part of the cart's chassis, bend two wheel housing braces and butt weld them to the top of the outside axle plates (Fig. 13-5). These braces will strengthen the axles and will bolt to the cart's box later through holes drilled in the flattened pipe ends.

DIFFERENT SHAFTS FOR DIFFERENT HORSES

The other part of the cart's chassis consists of the two shafts and four braces to keep the shafts solid. You'll notice from the directions in Fig. 13-4 that the bends for the shafts are not simply right angles, and there are three possible places to cut the pipe to length. This is

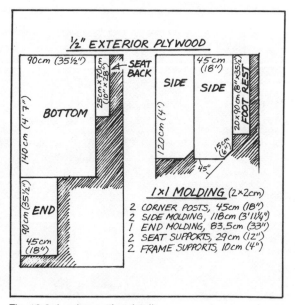

Fig. 13-3. Lumber cutting details.

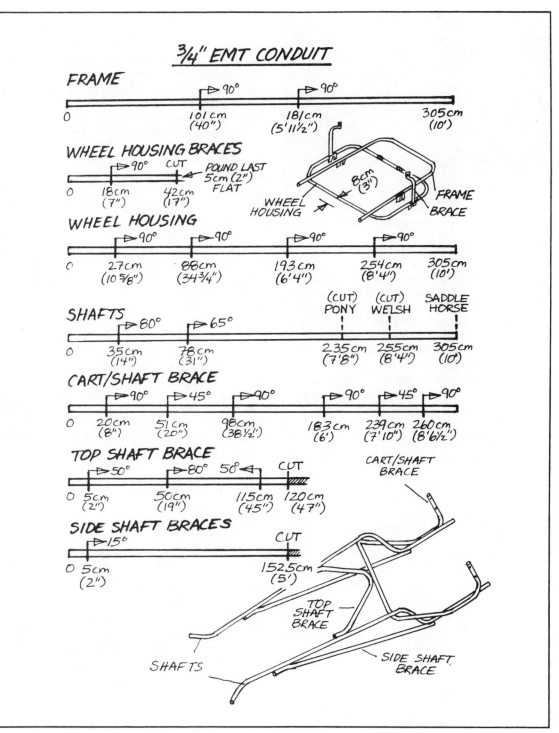

3/4" EMT CONDUIT

FRAME
- 0
- 90° — 101 cm (40")
- 90° — 181 cm (5'11½")
- 305 cm (10')

WHEEL HOUSING BRACES
- 0
- 90° — 18 cm (7")
- CUT — 42 cm (17")
- POUND LAST 5 cm (2") FLAT

WHEEL HOUSING — 8 cm (3") — FRAME BRACE

WHEEL HOUSING
- 0
- 90° — 27 cm (10 5/8")
- 90° — 88 cm (34 3/4")
- 90° — 193 cm (6'4")
- 90° — 254 cm (8'4")
- 305 cm (10')

SHAFTS
- 0
- 80° — 35 cm (14")
- 65° — 78 cm (31")
- (CUT) PONY — 235 cm (7'8")
- (CUT) WELSH — 255 cm (8'4")
- SADDLE HORSE — 305 cm (10')

CART/SHAFT BRACE
- 0
- 90° — 20 cm (8")
- 45° — 51 cm (20")
- 90° — 98 cm (38½")
- 90° — 183 cm (6')
- 45° — 239 cm (7'10")
- 90° — 260 cm (8'6½")

TOP SHAFT BRACE
- 0
- 50° — 5 cm (2")
- 80° — 50 cm (19")
- 50° — 115 cm (45")
- CUT — 120 cm (47")

CART/SHAFT BRACE

SIDE SHAFT BRACES
- 0
- 15° — 5 cm (2")
- CUT — 152.5 cm (5')

TOP SHAFT BRACE

SHAFTS

SIDE SHAFT BRACE

Fig. 13-4. Details for bending ¾-inch electrical conduit.

Fig. 13-5. The finished frame has braces on the wheel housings to add strength when riding over rough ground.

because the shafts need to be custom fitted to suit the size horse you will be using.

Make the first bend for the shafts to about 80 degrees, so the mudguard and footrest can lean against the shafts at the same angle (Fig. 13-6). The second bend is listed as 65 degrees, but this is only an approximation. Check Fig. 13-7 for the height and width the shafts should have for your size horse. To match those dimensions you will have to bend the shafts about 65 degrees down. Also, you will need to angle the bend in very slightly so the shafts toe in at the front. Do your best, then hook the shafts onto the frame with couplings to check things out (Fig. 13-8). Bolt the wheels on the frame to get an accurate idea of how

high the shafts need to be to keep the cart level. You will probably be able to adjust the angles of the shafts a little bit by hand at this point. If not, there's no shame in trying again with another length of pipe. When you get them right, set the pipe bender up about 10 cm (4 inches) from the shaft ends. Bend them about 30 degrees to the side so they won't poke the horse in the ribs. You'll probably also want to attach a small U-bolt to the outside of the shafts for the shaft loops or hold-back straps, between 40 cm and 65 cm (16 inches to 26 inches) from the shaft tips, depending on your harness. If you punch and drill holes for this U-bolt only on the outside of the shafts and then weld them in place, there are no bolt ends sticking through that could rub on the horse's flanks.

Now the shafts are in place, but they're far too wobbly. Add four braces to strengthen them. The first one, the cart/shaft brace, bolts onto the side of the cart (where it provides a bracket for mounting the armrest later) and then cuts across the two bends of the shafts to reinforce them. If you bend the brace as described in Fig. 13-4, it should use up one entire 10-foot length of pipe and fit snugly along the outside of the shafts. It touches the shafts in six places. Weld all six joints and make sure that the two upright ends are far enough apart for the cart's box.

The top shaft brace comes next. It will determine how far apart the shaft ends are, so make the middle bend as large as is necessary for your size horse (the 80-degree angle is an approximation). It welds to the

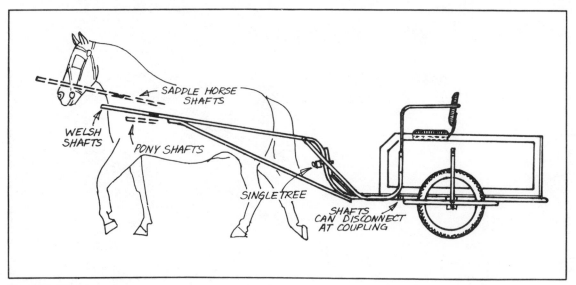

Fig. 13-6. Side view.

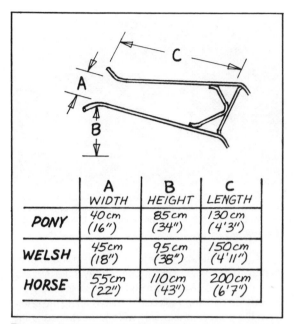

	A WIDTH	B HEIGHT	C LENGTH
PONY	40 cm (16")	85 cm (34")	130 cm (4'3")
WELSH	45 cm (18")	95 cm (38")	150 cm (4'11")
HORSE	55 cm (22")	110 cm (43")	200 cm (6'7")

Fig. 13-7. Dimensions of shafts for three sizes of horses.

cart in three places. The final two supports are the side shaft braces. Cut a 10-foot length of pipe in half for these braces. If you bend one end of each brace slightly, it will fit better for welding to the shafts. You may want to make these two braces slightly shorter for a small pony.

ASSEMBLING THE CART

Clean up all the welds with a steel brush and paint them to prevent rust. When the paint is dry, you can bolt on the pair of heavy motocross-type 20-inch bicycle wheels and connect the shaft assembly to the rest of the frame with two ¾-inch EMT couplings.

Set the box, footrest, and mudguard in place. The box attaches to the frame with two 2-inch stove bolts in the rear corners of the floor, two 2-inch stove bolts through the ends of the cart/shaft brace on the front sides, and a couple of ¼-inch × 1½-inch bolts through the flattened tips of the wheel housing braces in the middle of the sides. The mudguard mounts to the shafts with four 2-inch stove bolts. The footrest can't mount very well to the curved section of pipe on which it rests. Instead, make two 40-cm (16-inch) brackets out of ⅛-inch × 1-inch strap iron that mount to the bottom of the footrest with ½-inch panhead screws. Bend these brackets so they can also be screwed to the front of the mudguard and the underside of the

cart's bottom. The brackets must hold the footrest in place.

A padded seat is important if you plan to sit very long on a bouncing and jolting pony cart. You can pad the 1 × 12 lumber of the seat by cutting 1-inch foam rubber to size and stretching a piece of vinyl upholstery cloth that's 5 cm (2 inches) larger over it and over the wood. Staple or tack the cloth underneath. For a padded back, repeat this process with the seat back. Attach the seat to the cart with 1½-inch wood screws in predrilled holes in the seat support moldings. The seat should fit even with the top of the cart; this will leave plenty of room for cargo underneath.

The seat back screws to both the armrest and to the two strap iron brackets (they'll need to be about 30 cm or 12 inches long). The armrest can be cut and bent as shown in Fig. 13-9, then inserted 10 cm (4 inches) down into the open ends of the cart/shaft brace (½-inch conduit fits inside ¾-inch conduit). Bolt the armrest there before screwing the seat back in place.

The cart still must be attached to the horse, as he can't pull on the shafts. Many small pony carts have little hooks that fit holes punched in the leather traces or tugs, but this system is only strong enough for racing sulkies. We'll use a *singletree* instead, which also has the advantage of turning with the horse to prevent chafing on the breast pad or collar (Fig. 13-10). You can buy an oak singletree or make a perfectly suitable one yourself out of a 70-cm (28-inch) length of 2 × 4 lumber, tapered on both ends to 5 cm × 5 cm (2 inches × 2 inches). It connects to the cart with two heavy ⅜-inch eyebolts that have been linked eye-to-eye like a chain (I had to use pipe wrenches to open the eyebolt and a hammer to close it again). Bolt one of these to

Fig. 13-8. The shafts, braced for lightness and strength, attach to the frame with two couplings. The upright ends at left bolt to the cart's sides and serve as brackets to hold the armrest in place.

99

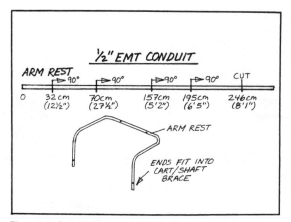

Fig. 13-9. Details for bending ½-inch electrical conduit.

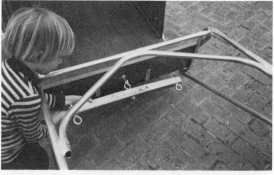

Fig. 13-10. The singletree, ideally made of oak, provides a way for the traces from the horse's harness to attach to the front of the cart; the singletree helps even the pull from the two sides.

the center of the singletree and one through the middle of the mudguard at the front of the cart. Then mount two more big eyebolts about 4 cm (1½ inches) in from the tips of the singletree and attach the horse's traces there. See Fig. 13-11.

HARNESS AND TRAINING TIPS

Harness can be bought in at least four sizes: midget, pony, Welsh, and horse. The smaller sets will have a light breast collar, while large sets often have the big stuffed collars used for workhorses. Make sure your bridle is equipped with blinders to keep the horse from being spooked by the cart behind him or other objects along the road. Another safety feature to look for is a *breeching strap*, which goes around the rear of the horse to keep the cart away from the animal's heels when going downhill or backing up. Sometimes leather thimbles are fitted over the shaft ends for this purpose.

A pony that has never pulled a cart will need to be trained to harness. This process may take several days or weeks. Accustom the pony to the harness without the cart and walk behind him holding the reins. Train the pony to make only wide turns (because the cart cannot turn sharply) and to come to a full stop at the voice command "whoa." For slowing down, use "easy" or "steady" and start with an audible "git up." Practice backing up, too (the sign of a proficient cart driver).

Introduce the cart gradually. Let the horse investigate it. Some trainers recommend rubbing the horse's sides with a broom handle first to accustom him to the feel of the shafts. Have someone hold the pony while you bring the cart up behind him and connect it. With your assistant leading the pony, walk him awhile with an empty cart before you climb aboard.

Hold the reins in both hands; for turns, move one

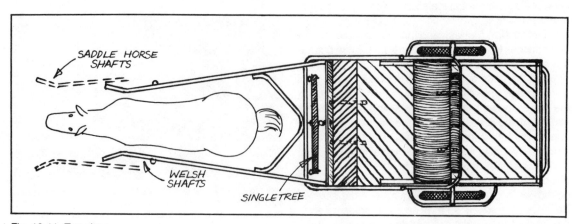

Fig. 13-11. Top view.

hand forward and the other one back. Do not loop or tie the reins to your hands, as this can be dangerous. It's also safest to walk and trot your horse in a confined area at first.

Once your horse builds up his wind, you'll be able to take heavier loads for longer distances. Balance the load so there is some weight on the shafts, but not too much. Remember: wheels are strongest—and can carry the biggest load—on even ground.

There's something special, and even a little romantic, about traveling in a pony cart to do the farm chores. Agribusinessmen may write it off as nostalgia, but it's more than that. Most of the people who are putting horses back to work behind carts and wagons weren't even alive when horse traffic ruled the roads. They've discovered that a horse can be outfitted to do *just about everything* around a farm for *much less* than it would cost to buy tractors and pickups for the same jobs. Whether you're interested in converting to horse power altogether or simply increasing the versatility of your saddle horse or pleasure pony, a simple two-wheeled cart is an inexpensive and practical first step.

Chapter 14

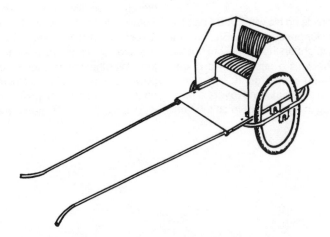

Dog Sulky

HERE'S A WAY TO PUT YOUR HOUND TO WORK AND give the kids a little fun, too. This sulky will fit any large, quiet dog or an average-size goat (Figs. 14-1 and 14-2). There's room for two small passengers on the padded seat. If they want to take a little load along, there's storage under the seat and in back. A powerful animal will be able to pull an adult or *three* children—with one standing in back.

The dog sulky is designed much like a scaled-down pony cart, but there are differences. Dogs are usually trained to respond to voice commands instead of rein control (Fig. 14-3). Seeing Eye dogs leading the blind and huskies pulling sleds learn to start, stop, and turn left or right at the trainer's word. An untrained pooch only responds to a choke chain, which should be enough to make him stop or go. If there are children in the cart, the only safe way to steer an untrained dog (or stop him if he spots a canine friend) is to have someone walk along beside him with the leash. If you'd like a little more speed, you can hold the leash while riding a bicycle next to the dog so he can gallop. One 65-kg (150-pound) Newfoundland has been clocked hauling *four* kids this way at a speed of 25 km/hour (15 mph).

There's little doubt that the kids will love the sulky,

but how about the dog? Most big dogs are so glad to get the attention and the exercise that they don't mind the harness. The cart itself rolls so easily that almost any dog large enough to fit the harness will be strong enough to pull it. A nervous or excitable animal will not do well with a load. If your hound has ever carried a backpack successfully, he's probably calm enough to get along with a sulky. Building the sulky is a three-step project: the frame, cart box, and harness (Table 14-1).

FRAME

The sulky frame is made from electrical conduit either welded or bolted together. Like all carts pulled in harness, this one has two long shafts that enclose the draft animal and keep the cart level. Because it would be awkward to store the sulky with the shafts attached, they're designed to unbolt from the rest of the frame (Fig. 14-4).

Mark three 10-foot lengths of EMT pipe (electrical conduit) for bends (Fig. 14-5). The frame that will support the cart's box is ¾-inch tubing while the wheel housing and shafts are ½-inch stock.

Cut the ¾-inch frame pipe to length and begin the first bend with the arrow on the head of your electri-

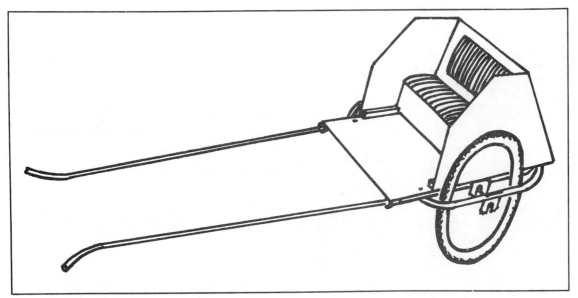

Fig. 14-1. The Dog Sulky.

cian's pipe bender lined up with the mark for bend A. Just bend the tip of the pipe up a tiny bit—enough that the shafts will angle in slightly when they're later fitted into the pipe end. Then move the bending tool to the second mark and make a 90-degree curve in the same direction as the first bend. Bend C is also 90 degrees in the same direction, but turn the bender around for the final bend. This is another very slight curve to match bend A on the other side.

The wheel housing is easy, because it's all 90-degree angles. If you can't get your hands on a ½-inch pipe bender, you can use the ¾-inch one here, too, without throwing the measurements off too much. Connect the pipe ends with a coupling and position the wheel housing on top of the frame so there's a 2.5-cm (1-inch) gap between the two chassis parts in the back. Then cut a scrap of wood to exactly 50.6 cm (20 inches) as a temporary spacer bar for the frame. Use it to make sure the frame's sides stay just that far apart until they're welded or bolted. Check the gaps for the wheels. These should be close to 9.5 cm (3¾ inches) wide on either side. If everything's in order, clamp it in place.

Next you'll need some plates to hold the wheels' axles. Make these from electrical box covers as described in Chapter 4, and clamp them in place. If you're welding or brazing, remember to brush and paint the joints to prevent rust. If you're bolting, follow the directions for the Freighter.

The shafts are basically straight sections of ½-inch pipe, but they curve out a bit at the front. The idea here is to allow the draft animal a little room to turn without having the end of the pipe jab him in the shoulder. Bend these pipes and fit them onto the cart by jamming them into the open ends of the frame's ¾-inch pipe. Because you've bent the pipe in the frame, the shafts only slide in about 15 cm (6 inches) before they stick tight. To make sure they don't work loose, drill holes and bolt them on with 1-inch stove bolts.

Now you're ready to mount some 20-inch front

Fig. 14-2. Even medium-sized dogs have no trouble pulling this easy-rolling sulky.

103

Fig. 14-3. Three-year-old Thwudly gets into harness for the very first time and does just fine. Untrained dogs will have to be led with a leash. With careful training, draft dogs will respond to voice commands.

bicycle wheels on the frame and see how it rolls. There is no need for heavy-duty wheels. If you can come up with a pair of used front rollers from kids' bikes, they'll do fine.

BOX

Cut ¼-inch exterior plywood and 1 × 1 molding for the box as shown in Fig. 14-6. If you have a table saw, you can rip your own molding from any standard lumber. Make sure it measures 2 cm × 2 cm (¾ inch × ¾ inch).

When all the parts are cut, lay them out on a table to visualize where everything goes (Fig. 14-7). All that molding will be mounted to the plywood with glue, clamped by ¾-inch wood screws (in predrilled holes through the plywood) and short nails. The seat support and seat back have moldings that fit flush along

Table 14-1. Dog Sulky Materials.

Frame	Box
1 10' length of ¾" EMT pipe	1 4' × 8' sheet of ¼" exterior plywood
2 10' lengths of ½" EMT pipe	10' of 1 × 1 molding
1 ½" EMT couplings	some ¾" wood screws and short nails
4 4" × 4" square electrical box covers	scraps of 1" foam rubber
(without "knockouts")	scraps of vinyl upholstery cloth
4 1" sheet metal screws with washers	2 small leather scraps
2 1" stove bolts	
2 20" × 1.75 front bicycle wheels	**Harness**
4 washers (for wheel axles)	19' of 1" nylon webbing
	20" (50 cm) of 2" nylon webbing
Additional for a Bolted Frame	2 1" slide buckles
4 ¼" × 2" bolts	4 snaps
8 ¼" × 1½" bolts	denim scraps (for thimbles)

Fig. 14-4. The Dog Sulky can be stored on end or with its shafts unbolted and removed.

their sides. The three 10-cm (4-inch) pieces stand up against the seat back for the seat to rest on. The long piece of molding goes flush against the back of the large plywood part that will be the cart's bottom. The two smallest blocks of molding go underneath the bottom to support it in the middle by resting right on the wheel housing.

That should leave just four pieces of molding. These go along the lower edge of the cart's sides. Then you can assemble the cart; I find it easier to put the bottom on last. Once the box is together, touch it up with a little sandpaper (be sure to round the plywood edges). An oil-base paint will do for the finish, but I prefer a brown stain. It only takes one coat and doesn't show the dirt.

You could just paint the seat and nail it on, but why not cushion it and fit it with a simple hinge so there's storage space underneath? It's easily done with a few scraps of 1-inch foam rubber and vinyl upholstery cloth (most upholsterers will sell suitable scraps inexpensively). Just cut the foam to size, cut the cloth about 4 cm (1½ inches) larger on all sides, and stretch the cloth over the foam so it can be stapled or tacked on the underside of the seat. Two leather scraps can then be stapled on to attach the seat to the box and make a

hinge so the seat can be lifted like a lid. While you're padding things, you can make a cushion for the back the same way. Use a piece of plywood as a backing for the upholstery. Attach the padded plywood with ¾-inch screws through the seat back.

The box can be secured to the frame. Use four 1-inch sheet metal screws set in 8-mm (9/64-inch) holes—one in each corner.

The cart is complete at this point, and even without a harness it makes a great little rickshaw for the kids (Fig. 14-8). They will have lots of fun pulling each other around the block. It only takes an hour or two to sew a harness that will get the dog in on the act, too.

HARNESS

It's a common misconception that draft animals pull on the shafts of a cart, much as a person pulling a rickshaw will hold the handle. Most carts are pulled solely by the traces or tugs of the harness. The shafts themselves are only loosely attached to the harness and act to keep the cart level and the animal facing forward.

A good harness must attach securely to the cart (or to a singletree on the front of the cart) and have a chest pad in front for the animal to pull against. You need loops to hold the shafts at the right height and straps around the animal to keep everything in place. Finally, there has to be some way to stop the cart from running over the puller when he stops suddenly or is going downhill. The harness described here has all of these features and one more: it attaches with snaps so a dog that's out of control can quickly be set free of the sulky.

Leather makes the best harness, but it's expensive and difficult to work with. Instead, let's use nylon webbing, a very strong and inexpensive material that can be sewn with an ordinary sewing machine.

You'll need about 6 meters (19 feet) of 1-inch webbing and 50 cm (20 inches) of 2-inch material. Start by cutting a 305-cm (10-foot) length of the narrower stock for the tugs that will attach to the cart. The cut ends of the material will have to be seared with a candle flame to keep them from fraying, as is true whenever you cut nylon webbing. Mount snaps near the ends of this long piece so that it can be quickly attached to the wheel housing of the sulky's frame. Most fabric stores will be able to mount the snaps or show you how. Then sew the 2-inch-wide webbing right in the middle of the long piece to make a chest pad for the dog (Fig. 14-9).

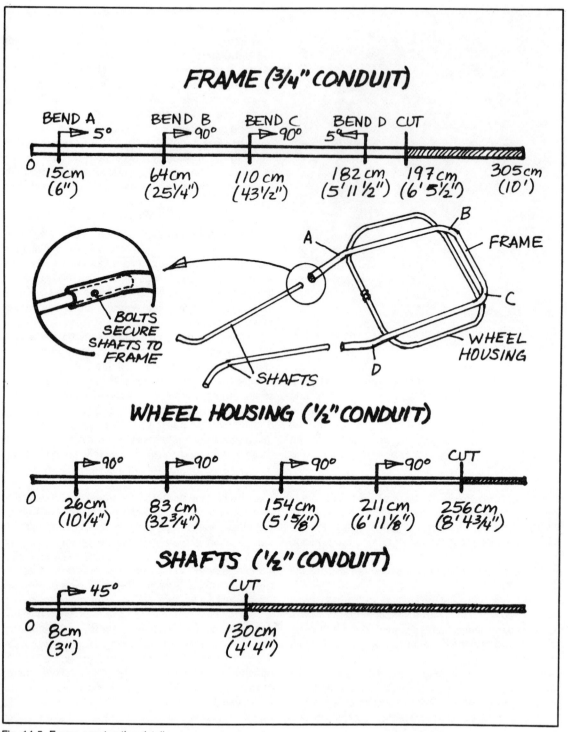

Fig, 14-5. Frame construction details.

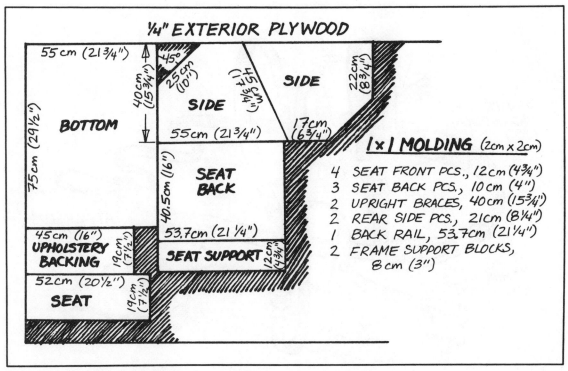

Fig. 14-6. Lumber cutting details.

At either end of the chest pad, sew on a buckle and strap to go over the dog's neck. Sew on another strap 15 cm (6 inches) further back that goes over his back and buckles behind his front legs. The measure-ments in Fig. 14-9 allow enough extra material that you should be able to tighten the harness with the buckles and have it fit almost any large dog. These straps around the animal are what won't fit if something is not

Fig. 14-7. With the molding attached, the plywood parts are ready for assembly. The seat and upholstery backing (at left) will be padded later.

Fig. 14-8. Long after the hound's gotten tired, kids still seem to have plenty of energy to give each other rides.

107

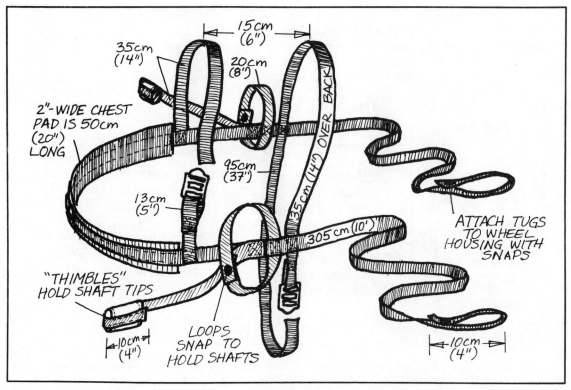

Fig. 14-9. A harness made of nylon webbing can be easily sewn on a home sewing machine in an hour or two. Check the measurements for the chest and neck straps on the dog you plan to use to insure a good fit.

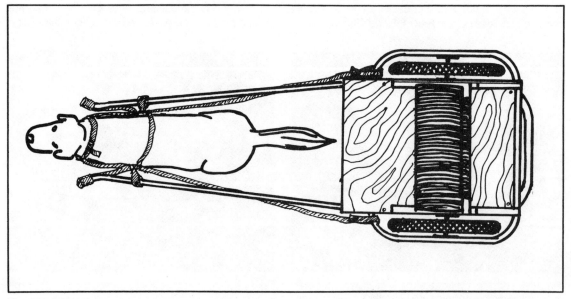

Fig. 14-10. Top view.

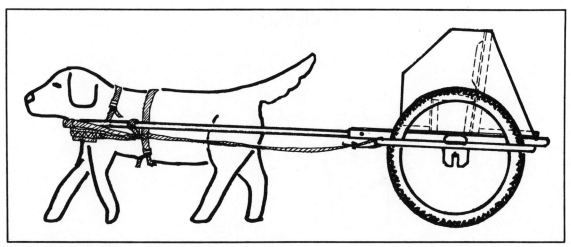

Fig. 14-11. Side view.

going to fit. You may want to pin them down and check before sewing them in place, particularly if you're using the sulky with a smaller dog, a sheep, or a large goat. The measurements allow for a 5-cm (2-inch) overlap when sewing on the buckles.

Sew on short loops to hold the shafts at the right height. I put snaps on these so the harness doesn't have to be threaded onto the cart each time it's used. Finally, sew some "thimbles" to cup over the shaft ends and keep the cart from rolling forward over the dog when he stops. You can make these out of jeans material sewn onto the webbing. To determine where

to sew the thimbles to the tugs, try it out on the cart. When the tugs are snapped to the cart frame and the thimbles are in place, the harness should slack a little, but not so much that the thimbles can be pulled off.

Now you're ready to try out the harness. Some people prefer to put the harness on the dog first, but I think it's easier to get the harness all set up on the cart and then lower it over the dog's head. I even leave the strap over his head buckled. There's only one buckle to fasten before he's strapped in. At that point, wherever he goes, the cart follows. See Figs. 14-10 and 14-11.

Chapter 15

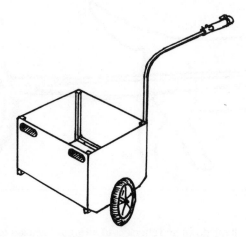

Wheelchair Cart

ANYONE WHO HAS BEEN CONFINED TO A WHEEL-chair knows how frustrating it is. It's tough to negotiate steps and curbs and maddening not to be able to carry more than will fit on your lap.

Imagine living within a block of a store but not being able to shop there because you can't carry the grocery bag home. You can't hold anything in your hands when you're using them to push the wheels.

What are the options? You can slip a backpack over the handles of the chair. This backpack is fine for a purse or a few books, but it won't hold many groceries. Likewise, a basket attached to the back of the wheelchair holds very little and is almost impossible to reach. Unfortunately, many handicapped people simply give up on hauling chores and rely on someone who can walk, regardless of how young, strong, or proud the invalid is.

This cart is designed to help the handicapped win back a little independence (Figs. 15-1 and 15-2). The cart makes it easy to pull *four bags* of groceries back from the store. It's small enough to be pulled down store aisles or through doorways. A flexible hitch made from a length of industrial hose allows the cart to swing directly *alongside* the wheelchair when the chair is turned sideways—letting the rider load and unload the

cart by himself (Figs. 15-3 and 15-4). When he gets home, he can disconnect the cart by himself by re-moving a hitch pin and slipping the cart handle out of the hose.

Laundry, potted plants, basketballs—all kinds of loads roll right along, almost without effort (Figs. 15-5). The load is really only limited by how much can be lifted into the cart with one hand; leaning over the side of a wheelchair with two hands is not stable enough for safety. Still, even grocery bags can be lifted with one hand if they are not too full or if they have handles.

Surprisingly, a cart has virtually no effect on the handling of a wheelchair. The cart neither makes the wheelchair more stable nor less stable. It does add momentum, however, making starts and stops slower with a heavy load.

This cart can be built for $15 in about five hours (Table 15-1). At a time when wheelchairs themselves cost between $300 and $1000, a homemade cart is a bargain.

WHEELS

This cart will probably never carry more than about 20 kg (45 pounds), so there's no need to fit it with heavy and expensive wheels. Wheels smaller than 20 cm (8

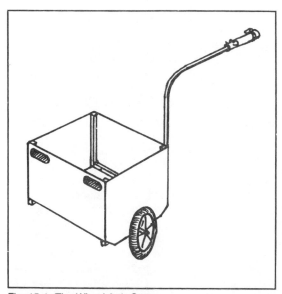

Fig. 15-1. The Wheelchair Cart.

Fig. 15-3. The cart's flexible hitch, made from a length of rubber hose, clips to the cart and attaches to the chair's handle with a hose clamp.

inches) in diameter might catch on bumps. The 8-inch casters from the front of a wheelchair are terrific (they have excellent bearings), but they are also very expensive. I find that 8-inch tricycle wheels stand up to the wear satisfactorily and are about five times cheaper.

Fig. 15-2. Rolling home from school, the student's cart is carrying the books. The Wheelchair Cart can give the handicapped a new sense of independence.

Fig. 15-4. A sharp left turn brings the contents of the cart within easy reach.

Fig. 15-5. There's room for groceries, books, or basketballs in this cart for the handicapped. It pulls easily without affecting the chair's balance.

Once you've got a pair of wheels, take them down to the hardware store to find an axle that fits them. Use threaded bolt stock for the axle; it comes in 3-foot lengths and 12 different diameters. Find one that just fits your wheels (probably 5/16-inch) and buy about eight nuts and washers that size, too.

Cut ¼-inch plywood and 1 × 1 molding for the box as shown in Fig. 15-6. Locate the front and back plywood pieces (they're the same size). Each of these pieces gets molding glued and screwed along three sides. Put the corner posts flush with either side, glue them, and clamp the glue with a couple of ¾-inch wood screws through predrilled holes in the plywood. Glue and screw the 51-cm (20-inch) molding along the bottom edge.

The two remaining pieces of molding go along the short edges of the bottom, and then the bottom can be attached to the front and back. Glue and screw the sides of the cart in place. Paint or stain all the wood parts and take a break while they dry.

To put on the wheels, thread some nuts and washers onto the long axle bolt and drop it into the slots in the cart's sides (Fig. 15-7). Tighten up nuts and washers on both sides of the two slots to secure the bolt. Next come the wheels. If you're bought the ex-

pensive wheels with bearings, slip them on and cinch them on with nuts. If your rollers have no bearings, you'll need to lock two nuts together on the bolt to let the wheel spin but keep it from rattling loose. In either case saw the bolt to length once the wheels are on.

HANDLE AND HITCH

The cart's handle is made from ½-inch electrical conduit available at the hardware store. Cut it to length and mark it as in Fig. 15-6. You'll need an electrician's pipe bender to bend it. If you can't borrow one, the hardware store people will sell you one for about $15. Set the arrow on the pipe bender's head on the first mark and bend the short end of the conduit up to a 90 degree angle. The second bend is the same direction, but at *right angles* to the first. Lay the first bend flat on the ground and hold the pipe bender vertically.

Before bolting this handle on, check that it will fit your wheelchair, because chairs come in a variety of heights and widths. If your chair has a handle in back, line the cart tongue up with it. If not, line it up with the top corner of the seat back. You can make a hitch later that will connect there. The cart should be level and just far enough away from the chair that it will swing snugly up alongside when the chair pivots to the left. If the cart's too far away, shorten the handle. If the cart tilts, bend the tongue up or down. If the cart does not follow right in the tracks of the wheelchair when it goes forward, bend the tongue left, or right until it does.

This ½-inch pipe is easy enough to work with that you can probably correct minor misalignments just bending it by hand. As long as you don't bend the pipe back and forth too much, it will be strong enough.

Table 15-1. Wheelchair Cart Materials.

Lumber
½ 4′ × 8′ sheet of ¼″ exterior plywood
11′ of 1 × 1 molding
Hardware
2 8″ wheels
1 3′ threaded bolt to fit the wheels
8 nuts and washers to fit the bolt
1 10′ length of ½″ EMT conduit
some ¾″ wood screws and glue
4 2″ stove bolts with nuts and washers
2 rear reflectors
20 cm (8″) of industrial hose (¾″ interior diameter)
1 hitch pin
1 large worm screw hose clamp
(or 2½″ C-clamp for chairs without handles)

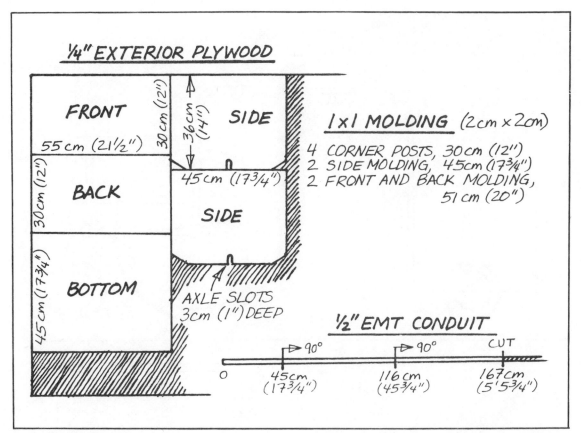

¼" EXTERIOR PLYWOOD

FRONT
55 cm (21½")
30 cm (12")

SIDE
36cm (14")
30cm (12")

45 cm (17¾")

SIDE

BACK
30cm (12")

BOTTOM
45cm (17¾")

AXLE SLOTS
3cm (1") DEEP

1 x 1 MOLDING (2cm x 2cm)

4 CORNER POSTS, 30cm (12")
2 SIDE MOLDING, 45cm (17¾")
2 FRONT AND BACK MOLDING,
51 cm (20")

½" EMT CONDUIT

O   45cm   90°   116cm   90°   167cm   CUT
(17¾")   (45¾")   (5'5¾")

Fig. 15-6. Cutting details.

The handle attaches to the cart with four 2-inch stove bolts—two through the front molding along the bottom of the cart, and two through the front corner post. It'll be easiest to drill holes for these bolts if you start by hammering an indentation in the pipe with a hammer and punch.

I'm going to describe more than one hitching arrangement, as wheelchairs come in more than one style. Although it is possible to hook onto the chair's armrests (Safeway supermarkets have developed a shopping cart with this method), it's surprising how many chairs do not have armrests. I think a larger percentage have handles in back, so let's look at a simple hitch that connects there first. See Figs. 15-8 and 15-9.

Get a 20-cm (8-inch) length of industrial hose (the kind used for washing machines) for this hitch. It should have a 1.8-cm (¾-inch) interior dimension that allows the ½-inch conduit of the cart handle to just fit inside. Stick the handle about one-third of the way into

Fig. 15-7. The wheels mount ot a solid axle that bolts to the underside of the cart.

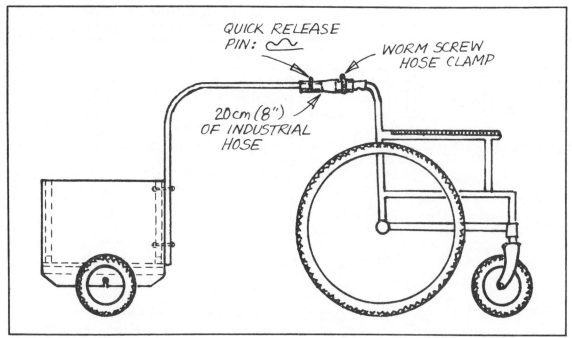

QUICK RELEASE
PIN: 〰

WORM SCREW
HOSE CLAMP

20cm (8") OF INDUSTRIAL HOSE

Fig. 15-8. Side view.

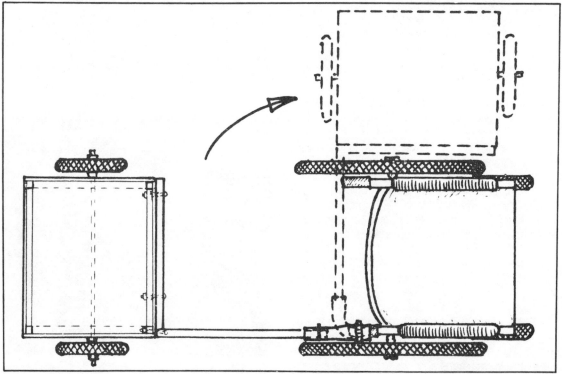

Fig. 15-9. Top view.

the hose and drill a hole through them both there. Make the hole big enough that a quick-release hitch pin can be slipped in easily to secure the hose, even with just one hand.

The other end of the hose will mount semipermanently to the wheelchair handle. The hose is too small to fit onto the handle as is, so slit the underside of the hose with a knife and *then* fit it over the handle. Clamp this solidly in place with a worn-screw-type hose clamp that tightens up with a screwdriver. The cart should now be attached firmly enough that it follows the chair without slack, but it still can be turned at a 90-degree angle either way.

This hitch won't do for wheelchair folks who have neither handles nor armrests on their chairs. For this group of self-confident wheelchair athletes, hitch the cart to the upper right-hand side of the seat back. There is a pipe here that's probably covered with up-holstery or padding of some sort, but clamp the hose of the cart's handle there anyway. By bending the split hose end down at a 90-degree angle, you can fit it around the upper end of this pipe. A worn-screw hose clamp won't work here, so you'll need to devise a different clamp.

This special clamp can be made out of a 2½-inch C-clamp and a short piece of 1-inch conduit. Clamp the C-clamp onto the pipe and weld both sides of its jaws to the conduit. Be careful not to weld up the threads or to weld the swivel jaw tight. Then cut the pipe 2.5 cm (1-inch) on either side of the clamp. Saw the pipe *lengthwise*, leaving the C-clamp with half-round pieces of pipe on both jaws. Clean and paint the welds, and use this little device to clamp the cart's hose hitch to your wheelchair. A drop of oil on the clamp's swivel jaw and threads will keep them working smoothly, so that the rider can attach the clamp by himself.

Index